30 SIMPLE
BLOCK

Other Titles of Interest

30 SIMPLE IC TERMINAL BLOCK PROJECTS

by

R. BEBBINGTON

BERNARD BABANI (publishing) LTD
THE GRAMPIANS
SHEPHERDS BUSH ROAD
LONDON W6 7NF
ENGLAND

Please Note

© 1996 BERNARD BABANI (publishing) LTD

First Published – June 1996

British Library Cataloguing in Publication Data

A catalogue record for this book is available from the British Library

ISBN 0 85934 379 0

Cover Design by Gregor Arthur

Printed and bound in Great Britain by Cox & Wyman Ltd, Reading

Preface

This book is the next logical step from BP378 *45 Simple Electronic Terminal Block Projects*, by the same author and publisher as this book, which describes an easy method of constructing transistor circuits without the need for soldering – an 'open sesame' to the practical world of electronics for youngsters or beginners. Having mastered a number of basic circuits using discrete components, these projects provide 'hands on' experience with some popular integrated circuits (IC), again using the plastic screw-terminal blocks, widely referred to by electricians as 'chocolate blocks'.

Although integrated circuits are more ambitious than single transistor circuits, as most of the components are packed in the ICs, the external wiring required is often simpler. For instance, twenty-three transistors, two diodes and sixteen resistors are packed in the 'centimetric' 555 timer IC used for a number of these projects. Integrated circuits are not only much smaller than their discrete counterparts, but demand far less current. Consequently, all projects are battery-powered, an essential safety feature for beginners.

Not all the external components are obligingly supplied with wire ends that will push into a terminal block so the constructor must prevail upon a friend or relative to do some initial soldering if hot irons are declared a 'no-go' area. Full instructions on making up the IC-breadboards are given in Chapter 1 CONNECTIONS AND COMPONENTS.

Armed with a layout diagram showing the actual physical shape of the components and instructions, most projects can be constructed within a matter of minutes. A small list of components is found at the end of each project, made up from a nucleus of common items, allowing them to be re-used for many other projects.

Many circuits can be easily modified for experimentation, or extended as modular units. Since the wire ends do not have to be cut and soldered, external components can be used again and again.

Typically, battery supplies and holders are fitted with wire-ended clips. However, components that are not wire-ended, for example, potentiometers, loudspeakers, thyristors, etc., can be wire-wrapped, or better still, soldered if possible. Short, flexible leads on these few components will pay dividends when you come to connect them into the terminal block projects.

As the book is also aimed at younger readers and beginners, simplified instructions are given for those not familiar with electrical and electronic components and circuits.

In addition to the block wiring layout showing physical and connections, the circuit diagram is included to familiarise readers with component symbols and circuit conventions.

Roy Bebbington

Contents

Chapter 1

CONNECTIONS AND COMPONENTS

All 30 projects use either 8-pin, 14-pin or 16-pin integrated circuits so it is advisable to make up three separate breadboard layouts, one for each type of IC. For convenience, the terminal blocks TB1, TB2, and d.i.l. holders for the ICs, should be mounted on a piece of plywood or chipboard measuring approximately 15×10 cm. This means that the layout diagrams for the projects are generally shown full size.

The 12-way plastic terminal blocks are available from most electrical shops and DIY stores, in 2A and 5A versions. The smaller size is useful when connecting leads, for instance, on transistors, are fairly short. The blocks can be either screwed or tacked to the board; the short plastic-covered copper leads from the terminals to the IC-holder are sufficient to ensure that the IC is held rigidly. The three layouts together with the pin numbering for the relevant ICs are shown in Figures 1, 2, and 3. Note that the inner terminals are used mainly for the IC pin connections, the outer terminals being used for components and supply connections.

The wire ends on resistors, capacitors, diodes, LEDs, transistors, etc., will in most cases be long enough to bridge the screw-in connections shown in the layout diagrams. Where necessary, additional terminal strips can be added to accommodate extra long connections. Additional two-terminal, single-way strips can be used if required to extend component leads. For clarity, some of the connection wires on the layout diagrams are shown extra long. However, it is advisable to keep all leads as short as practical; let them cross over the IC if necessary. Use plastic-covered wire for the links to prevent short-circuits, but make sure that the ends are trimmed back so that the copper wire is firmly gripped by the terminal screw. A small, flat-bladed screwdriver should be selected that suitably matches the diameter of the terminal screw-heads. If more than one IC is used in a circuit, a breadboard can be made up with two ICs wired between TB1 and TB2, or alternatively, two separate breadboard layouts can be linked.

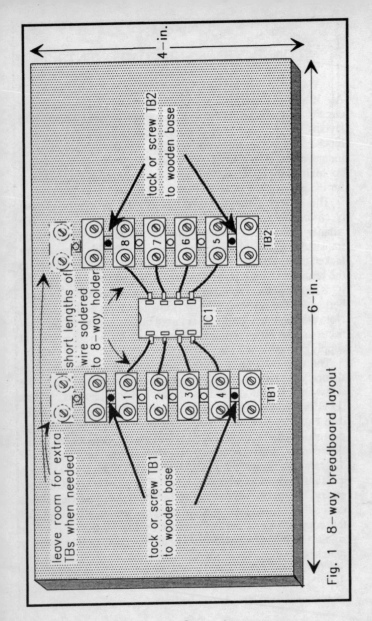

leave room for extra TBs when needed

short lengths of wire soldered to 8-way holder

tack or screw TB2 to wooden base

tack or screw TB1 to wooden base

4-in.

6-in.

8

7

6

5

TB2

1

2

3

4

TB1

IC1

Fig. 1 8-way breadboard layout

2

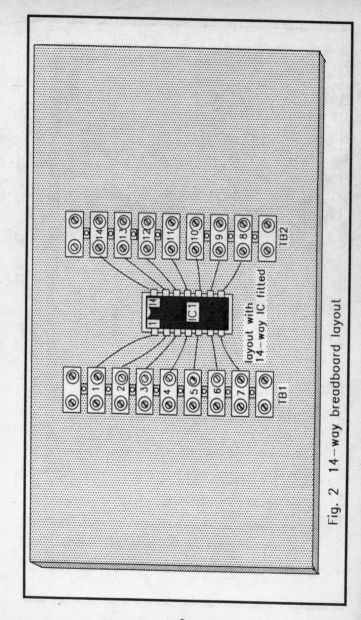

Fig. 2 14—way breadboard layout

3

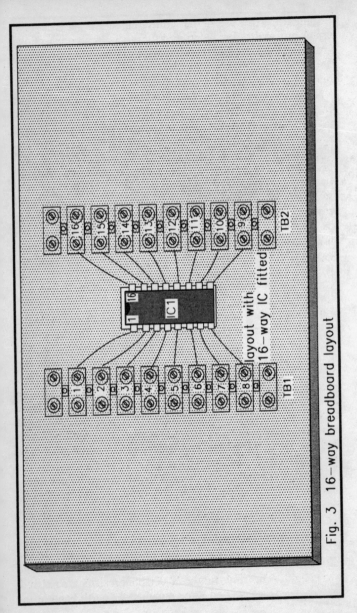

Fig. 3   16-way breadboard layout

4

Some ICs do not use all the connecting pins. If necessary, the surplus terminal(s) can be utilised for other circuit connections if required by simply unscrewing and disconnecting the redundant flying lead attached to the IC holder. This lead can be coiled up so that it does not short-circuit any connections.

Naturally, the projects would look neater and be far less bulky if the components were assembled and soldered on to circuit boards. Soldering is not the awesome task that many imagine, and it is hoped that after whetting the appetite for project-building, the chocolate block layout will be replaced by conventional wiring techniques. Each project includes a circuit diagram from which experienced constructors can work out their own practical design. Beginners are advised to compare each practical layout with its circuit diagram. In this way, students will soon become familiar with circuit diagram conventions and techniques. Once the practical implications are understood, projects can be constructed and adapted without the need for layout diagrams.

Component Identification

Most components can be identified from the annotation on the layout diagrams; e.g. R1 . . . for resistors, C1 . . . for capacitors, D1 . . . for diodes, etc. However, if you have bought a handful of pretty coloured resistors unless you are familiar with the colour-code you may have a problem. For readers who know it already, forgive the repetition; here is a reminder. Resistors are used to control voltages and currents in a circuit and are measured in ohms, thousands of ohms (k-ohms) and millions of ohms (M-ohms). To sort out your resistors, on page 6 you will find the code for the three end bands, based on the colours of the rainbow.

The first coloured band denotes the most-significant figure of the resistance value. The second band denotes the second significant figure, and the third band denotes the multiplier, i.e. the number of noughts that follow. For example, in the timer of Project 1, there are two resistors used: R1 – 1k (1000 ohms) and R2 – 22k (22,000 ohms). The three identifying bands for the 1000 ohm are brown, (1), black (0), red (2), i.e. one, nought and two noughts. The bands for the 22,000 ohm resistor are red, red, orange, i.e. two, two and three noughts. A fourth band at the other end of the resistor indicates the accuracy of tolerance of the resistor: gold ±5%, silver ±10%, not too important in these projects. Unless otherwise indicated, all resistors used in the projects in this book should be ¼ watt, 10%.

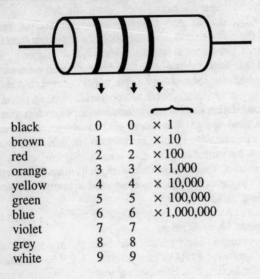

black	0	0	× 1
brown	1	1	× 10
red	2	2	× 100
orange	3	3	× 1,000
yellow	4	4	× 10,000
green	5	5	× 100,000
blue	6	6	× 1,000,000
violet	7	7	
grey	8	8	
white	9	9	

Chapter 2

555 TIMER PROJECTS

The 555 IC, mounted on an 8-pin dual-in-line chip, is a popular multivibrator for timing purposes or for pulse generation. It operates in three different modes.

In the monostable or one-shot mode it functions as a timer by reason of its one unstable state, the period of which can be controlled by varying the timing components.

In the astable (not stable) mode the 555 produces a continuous train of pulses and so functions as an oscillator, which can be used to generate clock pulses, to control LED indicators, or to produce audio outputs.

In the bistable or flip-flop mode the multivibrator has two stable states and will latch in one state until it is triggered into the other state.

All three of its modes are exploited in the following projects.

Project 1 – Timer

This general-purpose timer has a variety of uses around the house, from keeping board games on the move, to the more mundane culinary tasks such as egg-timing. The values chosen give a timing range selectable from about 0 to 15 minutes, but the timing components can easily be changed to suit specific requirements.

Circuit (Fig.4)

For this application, the 555 timer is employed in its monostable mode. At switch-on, the electrolytic capacitor C1 charges through a variable resistor network, to give the required time delay. This is its unstable state. When C1 has charged to about two-thirds of the supply voltage, the monostable reverts to its stable state and its output operates a buzzer.

In this simple circuit, the switch S1 not only serves as the on/off control but is also used to start and reset the timing sequence. At switch-on the timing capacitor C1 starts to charge

7

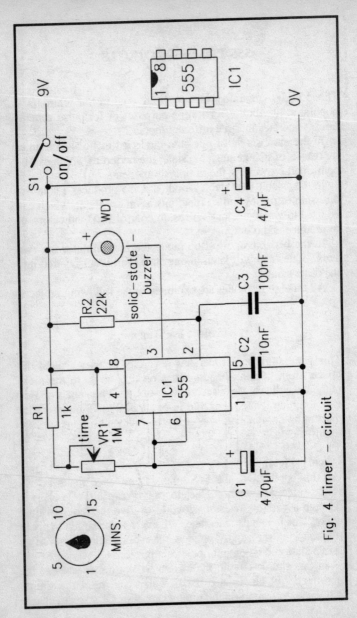

Fig. 4 Timer – circuit

8

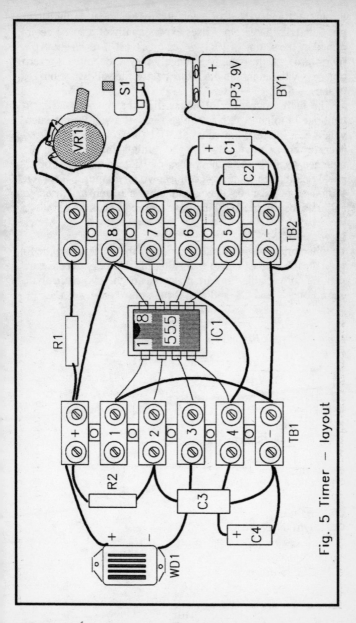

Fig. 5 Timer — layout

9

through R1 and VR1. Consequently, the potential on threshold pin 6 and discharge pin 7 rises exponentially at a speed determined by the setting of VR1. When pins 6 and 7 reach about 6V (two-thirds of the supply voltage), they are pulled to zero together with output pin 3. Consequently, the solid-state buzzer is activated.

The high value of VR1 means that the timer is easier to calibrate in minutes rather than seconds. If small timing intervals are of interest, the value of VR1 (or C1) can be reduced accordingly. Conversely, longer timing intervals can be obtained by increasing the values of VR1 and/or C1. For an evenly-calibrated scale, use a linear volume control for VR1. Various times can be checked against a watch and used to calibrate a scale of useful intervals, appropriate to its purpose.

Layout (Fig.5)
The diagram shows a suitable layout for the timer, using the 8-way breadboard with two 6-way terminal blocks. Make sure that the correct polarities are observed for the two electrolytic capacitors C1 and C4, and also for the piezo buzzer WD1.

Components for Project 1

Resistors
R1   1k
R2   22k

Potentiometer
VR1 1M potentiometer (linear)

Capacitors
C1   470µF elect. 10V
C2   10nF
C3   100nF
C4   47µF elect. 10 V

Semiconductor
IC1 NE555 timer

Loudspeaker
WD1 solid-state buzzer

Switch
S1   S.P.S.T. (on/off)

Miscellaneous
8-way breadboard layout, 9 volt battery (PP3), and clip.

Project 2 – One-shot

This project uses the unstable state of the 555 to provide a controlled width one-shot pulse of fixed amplitude. This can be used to trigger counters and games where identical single-event pulses are required, or as a bounce-free switch. The output pulse width with the timing components given is about one-fifth of a second.

Circuit (Fig.6)
The circuit diagram is similar to that of the timer in Project 1 except for component values and the output arrangement. However, note that contacts are now used to provide the trigger input to IC1 pin 2. These contacts may be a 'make' switch, a magnetic reed switch or a light-dependent resistor (l.d.r.) depending on the application. When the contacts close, the trigger (pin 2) goes low, and a positive-going output pulse occurs on pin 3. The duration of this pulse is determined by the time constant of R1, C1. Increasing the value of C1 to 10µF – a factor of ten – will increase the pulse width to about two seconds. Any further closures of the trigger contacts during the pulse output will be ineffective. A light-emitting diode D1 and a series current-limiting resistor R3 have been included to give a visual indication of the output pulse. These may be omitted if desired when the one-shot circuit has a practical application. For example, this one-shot could be used instead of the IC1 circuit in Project 20 'Trigger happy' game.

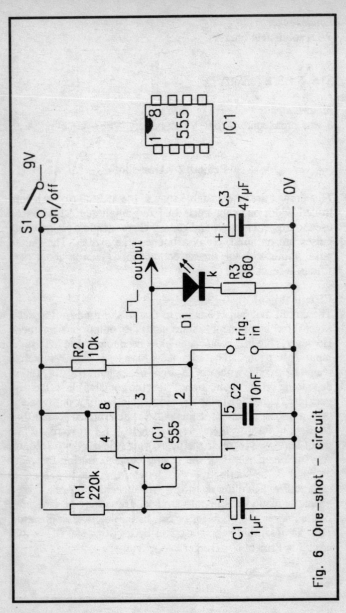

Fig. 6 One-shot – circuit

12

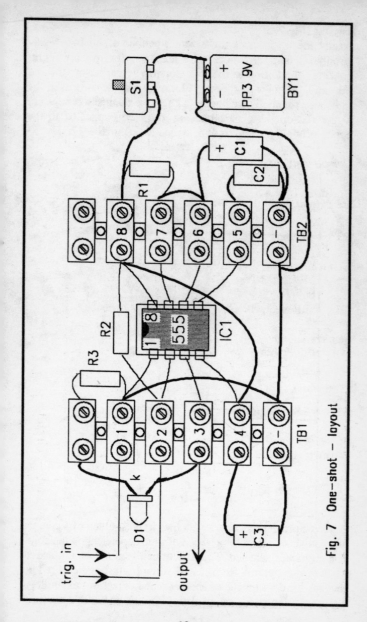

Fig. 7 One-shot – layout

13

Layout (Fig.7)

Again, the layout uses the 8-way breadboard and two 6-way terminal blocks are more than adequate for the few components. In addition to the two electrolytic capacitors C1 and C3, the light-emitting diode (LED) must also be connected the right way round. The cathode (k), i.e. the connection adjacent to the flat on the plastic housing, must be connected to the upper terminal on TB1 and the anode to terminal 3.

Components for Project 2

Resistors
R1   220k
R2   10k
R3   680 ohms

Capacitors
C1   1μF elect. 10V
C2   10nF
C3   47μF elect. 10V

Semiconductors
IC1   NE555 timer
D1   LED

Switch
S1   S.P.S.T. (on/off)

Miscellaneous
8-way breadboard layout, 9 volt battery (PP3) and clip.

Project 3 – Touch Alarm

Here is a project that operates at the slightest touch of a contact and sounds an alarm for a period of time dependent on the component values selected. This circuit can usefully be employed as an intruder alarm, for instance, when Light-fingered Freddie touches the door handle or another metal object, for example, a chain securing goods on display. Although an audible alarm is shown, there is no reason why an LED cannot be included in the output to give a remote visual indication.

Circuit (Fig.8)

The touch alarm circuit uses the 555 in its monostable mode. The selected values give an audible output of about 15 seconds, but this delay period can be changed to suit individual preferences. A table giving some approximate timing values is shown, but if a longer alarm period is required, R1 can be increased to 1 megohm; with this resistance value and 100µF for C1 the alarm will sound for about 3 minutes. If a variable alarm time is required for a particular application, replace R1 by a variable resistor, e.g. VR1 used in Project 1.

With S1 switched on, when the contact on pin 2 is connected to the 0V line (via skin resistance), the timing cycle begins and the capacitor C1 charges exponentially through R1 at a rate depending on the values of these components. During this period (the unstable state), output pin 3 is high and consequently, the solid-state buzzer is activated.

When C1 is charged to about 6V, pins 6, 7 and the output pin 3 are short-circuited to zero as the circuit returns to its stable state, and the buzzer is de-activated. Notice that in this project the buzzer is returned to the 0V rail, i.e. it is activated for the unstable period, unlike in Project 1 where the buzzer is activated after the delay of the unstable period.

Layout (Fig.9)

The layout for the touch alarm shows the 8-way breadboard with two 6-way terminal blocks, which provide adequate space for the components.

Input pin 2 of IC1 and the 0V line should be connected to the touch contacts, which can be two adjacent metal plates insulated from each other that can be bridged easily by a finger or thumb. This can easily be arranged if the circuit is intended for normal use as a touch-activated switch, but as an intruder alarm the set-up requires a little more ingenuity to surprise any rascal with roving fingers. If the 0V line is earthed then a metal door handle, security chain, etc., connected to pin 2 may be sufficient to activate the alarm when touched. Check that the two electrolytic capacitors, C1 and C3, and the buzzer WD1, are

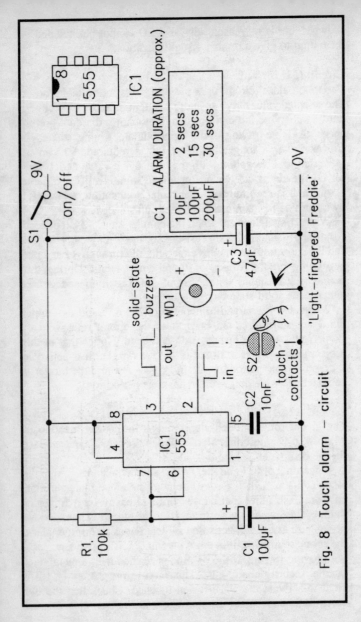

Fig. 8 Touch alarm – circuit

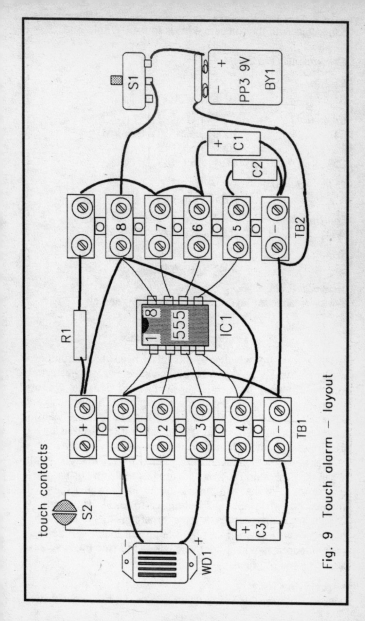

touch contacts

Fig. 9 Touch alarm – layout

connected with their negative leads to the 0V rail.

Components for Project 3

Resistor
R1   100k

Capacitors
C1   100µF elect. 10V (see text)
C2   10nF
C3   47µF elect. 10V

Semiconductor
IC1   NE555 timer

Loudspeaker
WD1   solid-state buzzer

Switch
S1   S.P.S.T. (on/off)

Miscellaneous
8-way breadboard layout, 9V battery (PP3) and clip.

Project 4 – Heads/Tails

It was a 'toss-up' whether to call this a heads/tails circuit or a red/green winker as it can be both. This electronic heads/tails simulator, although much larger than a coin, does not get lost, or come down on its end in the long grass. Simply push and release a button and a red or a green LED will indicate heads or tails respectively. Board games can easily be devised using red and green opponents based around this project.

Normally, both the red and green LEDs will light dimly when the pushbutton is operated, too fast to distinguish as alternate flashes, so that it is impossible to judge which light will remain on when the pushbutton is released. However, by changing the time constants the alternate green and red flashes can be slowed down. This might be useful to add a little skill, or to impose a handicap for those with a little too much skill, in selecting red or green.

Circuit (Fig.10)
This circuit uses the 555 in its astable mode. When pushbutton

S2 is operated the circuit oscillates as capacitor C1 charges via R1, D1, and discharges via D2, R2, repeatedly. The values chosen for C1 and R1, R2 are such that the red and green LEDs, D3, D4, flash at several hundred times per second when pushbutton S2 is pressed. With R1 equal to R2, the mark/space ratio of the output square-wave is 1:1, giving an even chance of a head or tails result when S2 is released.

The square-wave output on pin 3 alternately drives the two LEDs series-connected with their current-limiting resistors, R3, R4, between 0V and 9V. If the circuit is interrupted (S2 released), it latches in whatever state it is in at that instant. When the output is on the negative half-cycle, only D3, the red LED (heads) is activated; on the positive half-cycle, only D4, the green LED (tails) is activated.

Variations

A variety of other uses spring to mind for this project, e.g. a duple-time metronome, an intruder deterrent, a twinkling decoration, etc. All these uses would require a slower oscillator speed and C1 could be increased to several microfarads and R1 replaced by a 1M variable resistor.

To make a twinkling decoration, connect four LEDs in parallel with D3, four LEDs in parallel with D4, and reduce the values of resistors R3 and R4 to say 120 ohms.

Layout (Fig.11)

The layout for the heads/tails project needs an extra terminal connection to accommodate all components. This could of course be a single two-way block, but as shown, TB1 is now a 7-way connector. The extra connection at the top has been added to secure diode D2 and resistor R2. In fact, there are sufficient existing terminals available, but it was decided to add an extra one to avoid confusion. Terminal TB2-5 is not being used. Alternatively, the two components, D2 and R2, can be secured on TB2-5, if the wire link to IC1-5 is disconnected and insulated.

Components for Project 4

Resistors

R1, R2	27k (2 off)
R3, R4	470ohms (2 off)

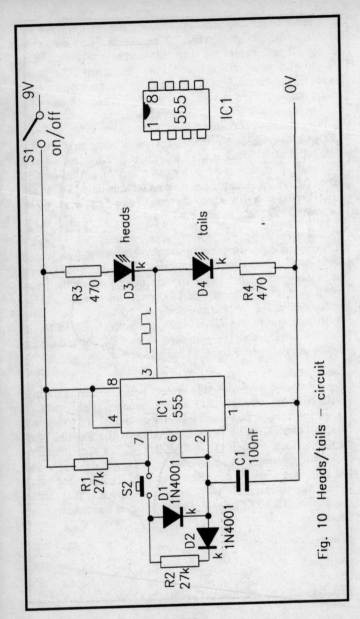

Fig. 10 Heads/tails — circuit

20

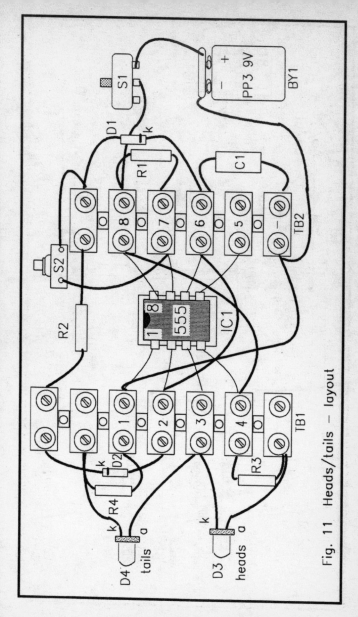

Fig. 11 Heads/tails – layout

21

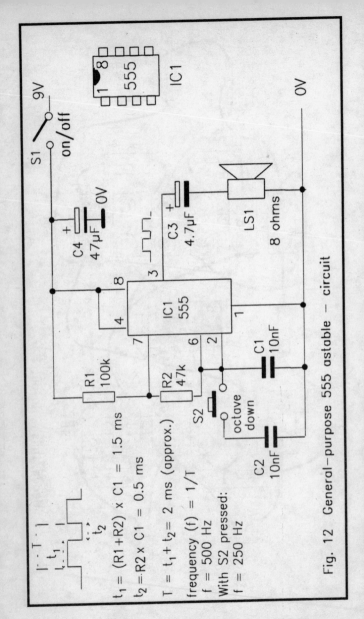

$t_1 = (R1+R2) \times C1 = 1.5$ ms

$t_2 = R2 \times C1 = 0.5$ ms

$T = t_1 + t_2 = 2$ ms (approx.)

frequency (f) = 1/T

f = 500 Hz

With S2 pressed:

f = 250 Hz

Fig. 12 General–purpose 555 astable – circuit

22

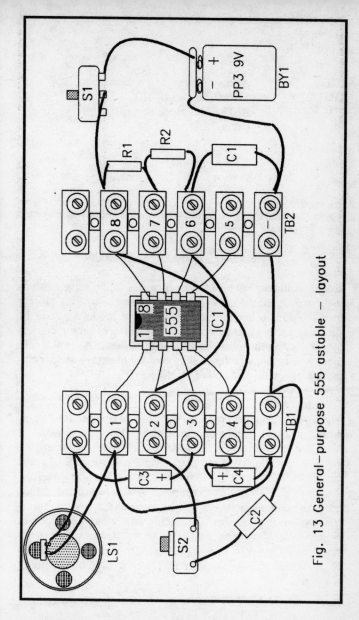

Fig. 13 General-purpose 555 astable — layout

23

Capacitor
C1   100nF

Semiconductors
IC1   NE555 Timer
D1, D2   1N4001 diodes (2 off)
D3   Red LED
D4   Green LED

Switches
S1   S.P.S.T. (on/off)
S2   Push -to-make 9non-locking)

Miscellaneous
7-way breadboard, 6-way breadboard, 9V battery (PP3) and
clip.

Project 5 – General Purpose Astable

Audio oscillators have a number of useful functions as calibration sources, tone generators, audible alarms, etc. This project uses the 555 in its free-running mode, to produce a train of square or rectangular pulses. Extra switching of timing capacitors or varying the timing resistor suggest the basis for a simple electronic organ, which could be coupled to octave divider circuits (Project 29) and power amplifiers (Project 26).

Circuit (Fig.12)

The circuit diagram represents the basic astable multivibrator, which produces a train of rectangular pulses at output pin 3. Note that the pushbutton S2 (locking or non-locking depending on the application) adds an extra timing capacitor C2 of equal value in parallel with C1, to produce an 'octave down' facility. This is merely shown as an example, and, as suggested, different values of capacitance can be switched in by additional pushbuttons to give other frequencies, thus forming the basis of a simple electronic organ. Alternatively, different values of R1 could be switched in, or variable resistors used. The frequency of oscillation is approximately 1/RC as indicated on the circuit diagram.

Layout (Fig.13)

The layout of this astable only needs two 6-way terminal blocks for the arrangement shown, but if extra note-switching circuits are used then extra terminal blocks will be needed. If a volume control is required, a resistor of up to several hundred ohms can be included in series with the loudspeaker LS1.

Components for Project 5

Resistors

R1	100k
R2	47k

Capacitors

C1	10nF
C2	10nF
C3	4.7µF 10V elect.
C4	47µF 10V elect.

Semiconductor

IC1	NE555 timer

Loudspeaker

LS1	8 ohms

Switches

S1	S.P.S.T. (on/off)
S2	push-to-make (see text)

Miscellaneous

8-way breadboard layout, 9V battery (PP3) and clip.

Project 6 – Audio Guitar Tuner

This project does not claim to provide a sophisticated tuning standard, but offers a range of steady audio tones that can be calibrated to respond to the six open-string notes of the guitar (or tuning notes of other instruments). As a bonus, it can also serve as an audio oscillator.

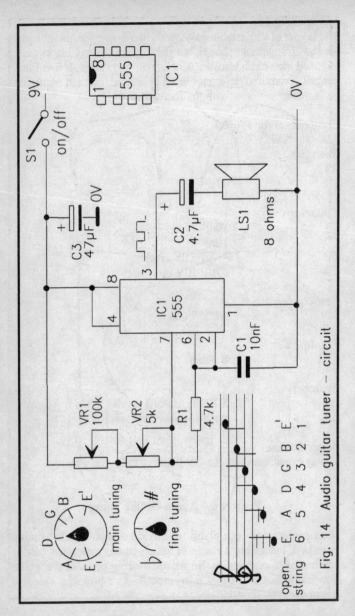

Fig. 14 Audio guitar tuner – circuit

26

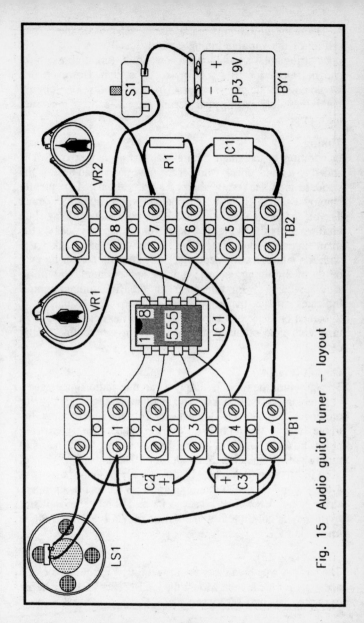

Fig. 15 Audio guitar tuner – layout

The main limitation is that accuracy depends on the correct setting of the variable tuning control. Ideally, each of the six open-string notes should have its own multi-turn tuning control and be selected with a six-way rotary switch. However, this would complicate the issue for a so-called 'non-solder' circuit, but is certainly worth considering for the serious constructor/musician.

Tuning

In addition to the main tuning dial, a fine tuning control is added as a quick check whether the note you sound against the standard is either flat or sharp. As a trombonist, I frequently employ a similar fine tuning technique when tuning to a piano. The pianist plays a B-flat, which I also play, adjusting my slide until we are both in tune. The degree of discrepancy seen on the main slide can then be transferred to the tuning slide. Likewise, with the guitar, having accurately selected an open-string note on the main tuning control, play the appropriate note with it. Any deviation from mid-point on the fine tuning control indicates whether the guitar is flat or sharp. The string can be tightened or slackened accordingly, until the note played is in tune with note obtained at the mid-point on the fine tuning control.

Circuit (Fig.14)

The circuit of the tuner is simply a variable audio signal generator feeding a loudspeaker. The frequency range required for the open-strings covers two octaves from the low E below the treble staff to the high E on the top space. The open-string notes, E, A, D, G, B, E, are calibrated around VR1, the main tuning potentiometer with a value of 100k-ohms. The control VR2 in series with this has a value of only 5k-ohms so acts as a fine tuning device. When calibrating VR1 to the six open-string notes, VR2 must be set to its mid-point. The oscillator frequency is controlled by the values of VR1, VR2 and R1 in series, and C1.

Layout (Fig.15)

The basic 8-way breadboard with two 6-way terminal blocks is adequate for the layout. Mount the loudspeaker LS1 on a baffle to improve its bass response.

Resistor
R1   4.7k

Potentiometers
VR1 100k (lin.)
VR2 5k (lin.)

Capacitors
C1   10nF
C2   4.7µF elect. 10V
C3   47µF elect. 10V
Loudspeaker
LS1   8 ohms

Semiconductor
IC1   NE555 timer

Switch
S1   S.P.S.T. (on/off)

Miscellaneous
8-way breadboard layout, 9V battery (PP3) and clip.

Project 7 – Visual Metronome

Here is a simple project for the budding musician that requires only a handful of components. Keeping to a strict tempo can be difficult for the learner and assessing the tempo in the first place even more of a problem. This metronome can be adjusted to give a visual indication on an LED of speeds from about 44 to 156 beats per minute.

Calibration
The variable resistor control can be easily calibrated against the second hand of a watch or clock. It is sufficient to count the number of flashes in half a minute and double this to mark off

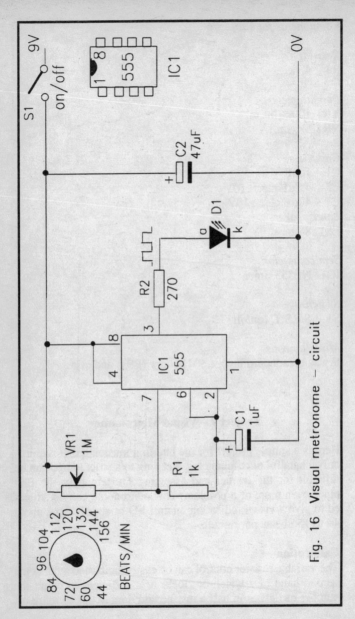

Fig. 16 Visual metronome – circuit

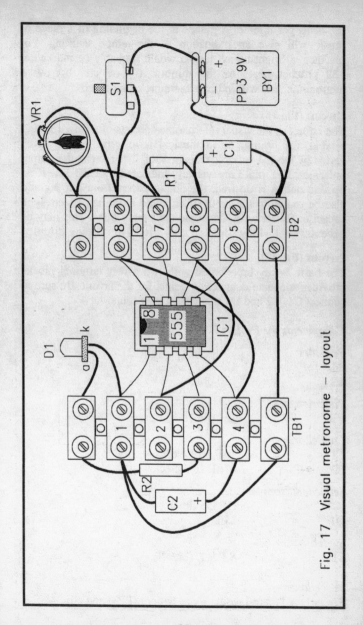

Fig. 17 Visual metronome — layout

the beats per minute. A glance at the beginning of a piece of music will give an indication of the tempo marking. For instance, a bright march tempo would probably be marked at 132 crochet beats to the minute. If you can borrow a metronome, this will indicate the more usual speeds.

Circuit (Fig.16)

The circuit of the visual metronome consists of a slow-running astable, the timing, or in musical terms, the tempo, being varied by the 1M variable resistor VR1. The rectangular output pulses on IC 1 pin 3 are visually indicated by LED D1. If an audible output is desired, the output pulses from pin 3 could also be routed to the input of an audio amplifier. Electrolytic capacitor C2 serves to decouple the supply lines. This may be necessary if long leads are used in these circuits.

Layout (Fig.17)

The basic 8-way breadboard with two 6-way terminal blocks provides adequate connecting points for the layout. Be sure to connect C1, C2 and D1 the correct way round.

Components for Project 7

Resistors
R1   1k
R2   270 ohms

Potentiometer
VR1   1M (lin.)

Capacitors
C1   1µF 10V elect.
C2   47µF 10V elect.

Semiconductors
IC1   NE555 timer
D1   LED

Switch
S1   S.P.S.T. (on/off)

Miscellaneous
8-way breadboard layout, 9 volt battery (PP3) and clip.

Project 8 – Flip/Flop Indicator

This simple bistable circuit requires only the 555 timer and two resistors for its change over action. A low input on either of two inputs causes the output to changeover, and stay in that condition until reset manually. Two LEDs are used with current-limiting resistors to indicate the flip-flop action. The input triggering can take many forms as suggested, e.g. the age-old zig-zag wire game, switch contacts for security, magnetic reed switches, light-dependent resistors, etc.

Practical Applications

In a practical circuit this change of state must have some application, so in this project a visual indication of the set and reset action is given by the addition of two different coloured LEDs connected across the output. Alternatively, a piezo buzzer could be connected in the output if audible indication of changeover is preferred.

The low inputs causing change of state must also have some practical purpose if the output indication is to be meaningful. For instance, in these days, when security is taken seriously, a triggered output could indicate visually and/or audibly that a contact has been closed by an intruder. In lighter vein, if the project is intended for a game, then a brief contact made by a coin or ball bearing against adjacent pins on a pinboard, or the touch of a ring held unsteadily when threading the perennial zig-zag wire-loop will trigger the circuit. Readers will no doubt think of other practical reasons for latching a momentary contact besides those suggested.

Circuit (Fig.18)

This simple circuit is shown together with some suggested trigger options. The two inputs of the 555 timer are pin 2, the trigger input, and pin 4, the reset input. Pushbutton S2 is used to reset the flip-flop for these applications, but for games where there are two contestants for instance, two similar touch controls could be used for each input for changeover purposes. The two output LEDs D1 and D2 should be of different colours for easy identification. The series resistors R3 and R4 serve as the current limiters.

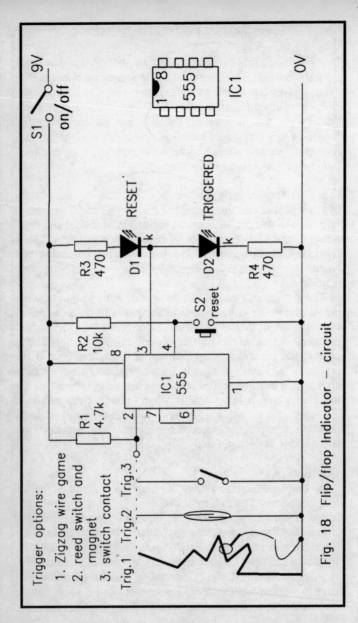

Fig. 18 Flip/flop Indicator – circuit

Trigger options:
1. Zigzag wire game
2. reed switch and magnet
3. switch contact

Trig.1 Trig.2 Trig.3

34

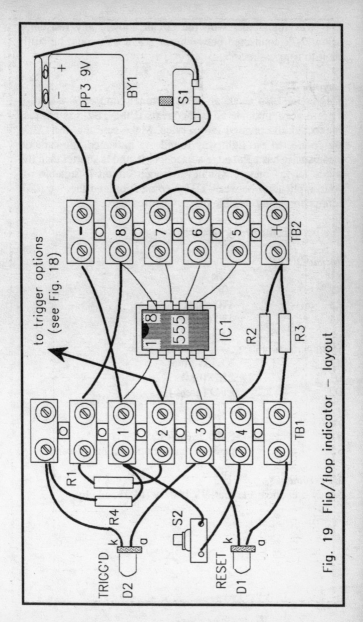

to trigger options (see Fig. 18)

Fig. 19 Flip/flop indicator — layout

It was found that with the circuit shown, any resistance below 2.7k connected between pin 2 and 0V would be sufficient to trigger the 555.

Layout (Fig.19)
This layout also needs an extra terminal connection added to TB1 to accommodate all components if the TB2-5 is not disconnected and pressed into service. Make sure that the LEDs are connected the right way round. As indicated, the cathode lead usually has a flat edge adjacent to it, and is shorter than the anode lead. Connect whichever trigger circuit is suitable for your application between TB1-2 connection and the –ve (0V) connection using flexible plastic-covered wire.

Components for Project 8

Resistors

R1	4.7k
R2	10k
R3	470 ohms
R4	470 ohms

Semiconductors

IC1	NE555 timer
D1	LED (red)
D2	LED (green)

Switches

S1	S.P.S.T. (on/off)
S2	push-to-make, non-locking (reset)

Miscellaneous
8-way breadboard layout, 9V battery (PP3) and clip.

Chapter 3

OP-AMP PROJECTS

The operational amplifier or op-amp as it is usually called, with its high gain performance has proved popular for a variety of uses, some of which are illustrated in the following projects. Originally developed for analogue computers, op-amps have made rapid strides since the advent of the silicon chip ICs. Besides finding numerous applications as a linear amplifier, this versatile chip, with its two inputs, inverting (–), and non-inverting (+), is ideally suitable as a comparator. Often a small input signal is compared with a reference signal to provide a switching action when the reference signal is exceeded.

The gain of an op-amp can be reduced by connecting a feedback resistor between the output and the inverting input. The smaller the value of this resistor the greater the feedback and the lower the overall gain.

Project 9 – Dusk/Dawn Switch

This project uses the 741 integrated circuit as a comparator. The sensor is a light-dependent resistor (LDR), which automatically switches on a small night light when daylight fades, or the bedroom light is put out. Alternatively, a slight wiring change can easily allow this circuit to be light-operated if you need some signal to indicate when 'morning has broken'. The sensor might need to be external for this application. Other fairly obvious security applications for this circuit are to indicate whether a light is switched on, switched off, or obstructed.

Again, although the output indicator is visual, a piezo buzzer could be substituted for the lamp.

Circuit (Fig.20)
The circuit operation is shown for dusk operation, i.e. the light is switched on if PCC1 is in shade. The sensor resistance varies widely, depending on the amount of light falling on it. Under light conditions the resistance of PCC1 is relatively low, and

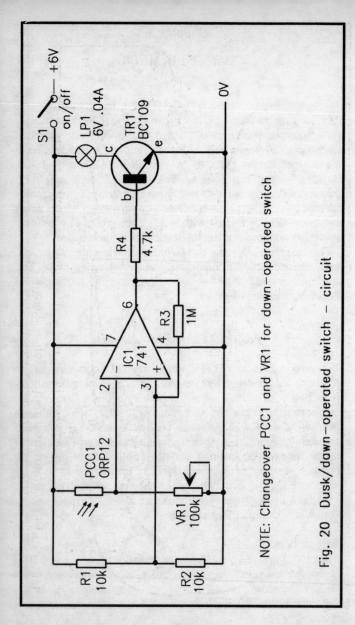

NOTE: Changeover PCC1 and VR1 for dawn-operated switch

Fig. 20 Dusk/dawn-operated switch – circuit

38

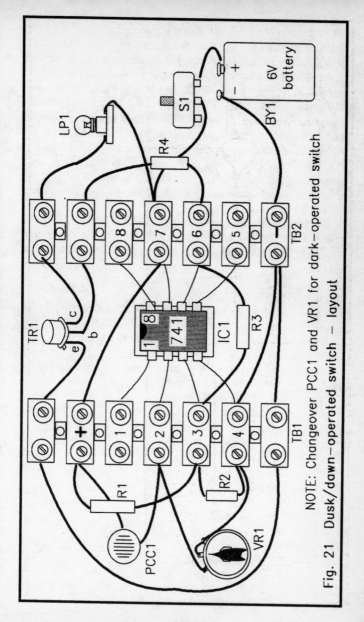

NOTE: Changeover PCC1 and VR1 for dark-operated switch

Fig. 21 Dusk/dawn-operated switch — layout

39

the voltage input at IC1 pin 2 (the inverting input) is held higher than the reference input by the setting of VR1. When darkness falls, the resistance of PCC1 increases sharply, the voltage on pin 2 falls below that of the reference voltage on pin 3 which makes output pin 6 positive. Via base resistor R4, this switches on transistor TR1 and LP1 lights. As the lamp takes 40 milliamps, a 6V battery, or four 1.5V AA cells in a battery holder will give longer life than a layer-type battery. The circuit is not self-latching, so in the circuit shown, if the light condition to PCC1 improves, LP1 will switch off. The circuit acts as a Schmitt trigger, resistor R3 giving a slight amount of positive feedback, which provides a snap action to the changeover point.

If a dawn-operation is required, then PCC1 and VR1 must be reversed. On the layout, it is necessary to take the upper connection of PCC1 to TB1-4, and the lower connection of VR1 to TB1(+).

Layout (Fig.21)
The layout shows two 7-way terminal blocks are needed for the 741 op-amp and the other components. The LDR, PCC1, may be extended with an extra 2-way terminal block and a length of flex for remote sensing.

To calibrate VR1, decide on the degree of light required for switchover and adjust VR1 accordingly for this point.

Components for Project 9

Resistors

R1	10k
R2	10k
R3	1M
R4	4.7k

Potentiometer

VR1	100k (lin.)

Lamp

LP1	6V 0.04A

Semiconductors

IC1	741 Op-amp
PCC1	ORP12 light-dependent resistor
TR1	BC109

Switch

| S1 | S.P.S.T. (on/off) |

Miscellaneous
8-way breadboard layout, 6V battery and clip.

Project 10 – Pressure Operated Switch

Although pressure mats are commercially available for use as a sensor in security systems, a piece of conductive foam plastic can quite literally be pressed into service for this purpose. This conductive foam is often used as packaging to protect ICs. Sandwiched between two small copper discs, this foam strip constitutes a variable resistance which is pressure-dependent. In a comparator circuit, this change of resistance can be used to switch on an indicator light, operate an alarm, or actuate a relay. If you have an ohmmeter you can easily check a piece of foam for conductivity.

Circuit (Fig.22)
The circuit shows the pressure switch VR1 controlling LED, D1, via IC1, and output transistor TR1. The 741 op-amp operates as a comparator. Under normal conditions, i.e. VR1 not pressed, VR2 is adjusted so that the voltage on input pin 2 exceeds that of input pin 3. With output pin 6 low, TR1 is switched off and consequently D1 is off. The circuit is activated by pressure on VR1, which reduces the resistance of the foam and increases the voltage applied to the non-inverting input, pin 3. The resulting positive-going output signal on pin 6 switches on transistor TR1 via base resistor R2 and lights D1.

Layout (Fig.23)
The layout is straightforward, but will need extended flexible leads depending on the position of the pressure switch. Two

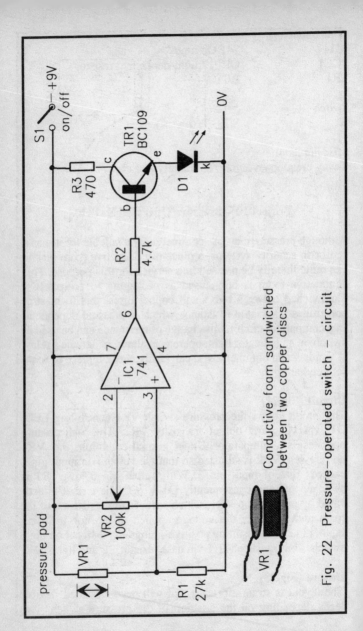

Fig. 22 Pressure-operated switch – circuit

Conductive foam sandwiched between two copper discs

VR1

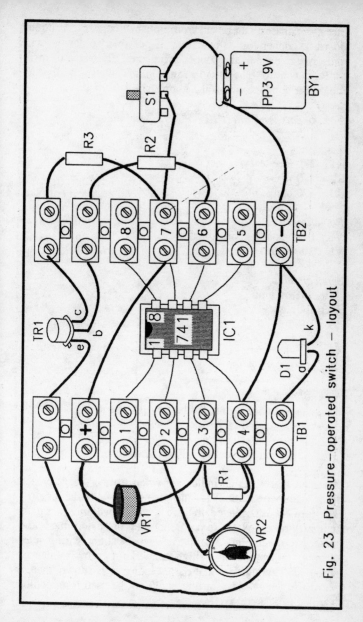

Fig. 23 Pressure–operated switch – layout

43

discs, or squares, can be cut from polished copper-clad circuit board or copper foil as available. If possible, solder the wire ends, one to each of the copper end pieces. The value of resistor R1 may need to be varied a few kilohms either way, depending on the conductivity of the foam strip.

Components for Project 10

Resistors
R1   27k (see text)
R2   4.7k
R3   470 ohms

Potentiometers
VR1 (see text)
VR2 100k (lin.)

Semiconductors
IC1   741 op-amp
TR1   BC109
D1   LED

Switch
S1   S.P.S.T. (on/off)

Miscellaneous
8-way breadboard layout, 9V battery (PP3) and clip.

Project 11 – Frost Indicator

A circuit that gives an indication when frost or ice is present finds useful applications for the keen gardener or the motorist. This project is arranged to give a visual warning when the temperature drops to zero, or another pre-determined low-temperature setpoint. Alternatively, by a slight wiring interchange, indication of a high-temperature setpoint can be arranged. Although a visual output indicator is shown, there is no reason why a piezo buzzer could not be used if an audible warning is desired.

Circuit (Fig.24)

In this circuit, the op-amp is connected as a comparator. The reference input is IC1 pin 3, which is held midway between the supply rails (+4.5V) because of the two identical resistors R1, R2, across the 9V supply. At normal temperatures the resistance of the thermistor TH1 (negative-temperature coefficient type) is relatively low, and the voltage input at IC1 pin 2 (the inverting input) is held higher than the reference input by the setting of VR1. At lower temperatures, when the thermistor cools, its resistance increases and the voltage applied to pin 2 falls below that of the 4.5V reference voltage. The more positive input on pin 3, the non-inverting input, produces a positive output on pin 6. A small amount of positive feedback via R3 gives a snap action effect to speed-up the changeover point. This positive output is applied via the base resistor R4 to switch on transistor TR1 which supplies current to the LED. The collector resistor serves to limit the current through D1.

Layout (Fig.25)

The layout requires two 7-way terminal blocks to accommodate the 741 op-amp and its associated components. Use plastic-covered wire for the additional links and make sure that no component leads are short-circuited. If temperatures need to be measured at a remote location then use an extra 2-way terminal block to extend the thermistor leads.

Calibration

For calibrating the freezing point, immerse the thermistor in iced water making sure that the connecting leads are kept dry. Potentiometer VR1 should be adjusted carefully until the LED D1 just lights. Check that D1 extinguishes when the thermistor is removed from the iced water.

Components for Project 11

Resistors

R1	10k
R2	10k
R3	1M

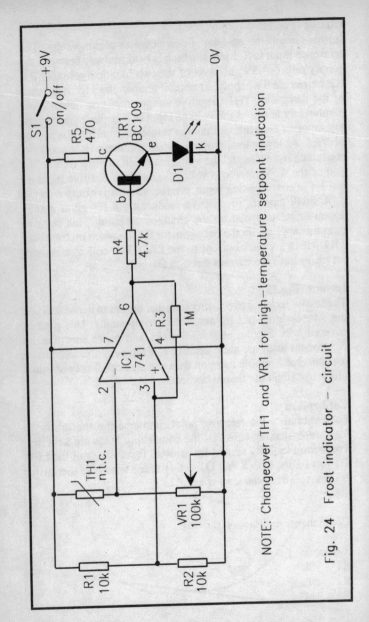

NOTE: Changeover TH1 and VR1 for high-temperature setpoint indication

Fig. 24 Frost indicator — circuit

46

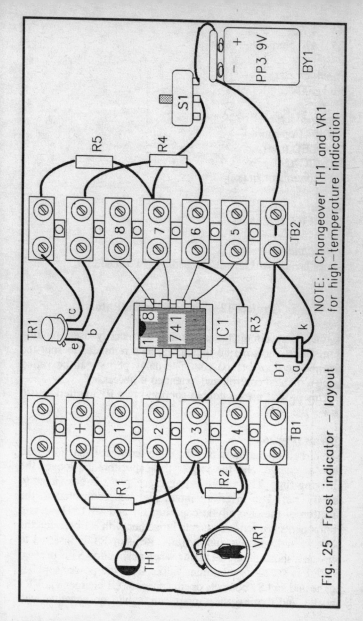

NOTE: Changeover TH1 and VR1 for high–temperature indication

Fig. 25 Frost indicator – layout

47

R4   4.7k
R5   470 ohms

Potentiometer
VR1 100k (lin.)

Semiconductors
IC1   741 op-amp
D1   LED (red)
TR1   BC109
TH1   thermistor (n.t.c.)

Switch
S1   S.P.S.T. (on/off)

Miscellaneous
8-way breadboard layout, 9V battery (PP3) and clip.

Project 12 – Time Delay Indicator

A time-delay circuit has a number of security uses, ranging from short alarm period indicators, to a reminder to shut the greenhouse door behind you. The delay period can be varied using a manual control, and extended if necessary.

This project uses a double supply – two PP3 batteries – to power the 741.

Circuit (Fig.26)
The circuit operation is based on the fact that capacitors take time to charge, and the bigger the capacitor, the longer the charging time. The non-inverting input, pin 3 is connected to the 0V rail. The inverting input, pin 2 is connected to the junction of the electrolytic capacitor C1 and VR1. These two components are series connected together with R1 between the positive and negative supply rails. Resistor R1 is inserted to prevent a short-circuit occurring when pushbutton S1 is pressed if VR1 is set to its minimum value. With the power supplies connected and S1 contacts open, capacitor C1 charges via VR1 and R1 and the inverting input, pin 2, will go negative with

respect to input pin 3 (0V). Consequently, output pin 6 goes high and D1 lights.

If the start pushbutton S1 is pressed, C1 is short-circuited and the positive voltage applied to pin 2 causes output 6 to go negative, switching off D1.

On release of S1, C1 starts to charge via R1 and VR1 and input pin 2 becomes more negative. When the transfer voltage is reached the negative input on pin 2 makes output pin 6 sufficiently positive to light D1. The delay will depend on the value of the resistance set on VR1; the greater the resistance, the longer the delay before the LED lights again. For alarm purposes, it may be preferable to have the LED on during the delay time rather than off. If so, simply remove the bottom end of R2 from the 0V rail to connect it to the +9V rail (TB1-3 to TB2-7 on the layout) and reverse the LED connections.

A 1M linear potentiometer for VR1 would give a ten-fold increase for the delay time, i.e. approximately five minutes.

Layout (Fig.27)
All the components can be easily accommodated on two 6-way terminal blocks. The leads to 'start' switch S1 will probably be extended depending on the particular application. An extra 2-way terminal block can be used for this purpose.

The time delay on VR1 can be indicated on a scale, which can be easily calibrated using a switch.

Components for Project 12

Resistors
R1   1k
R2   470 ohms

Potentiometer
VR1 100k (lin.)

Capacitor
C1   470µF 10V elect.

Semiconductors
IC1   741 op-amp
D1   LED

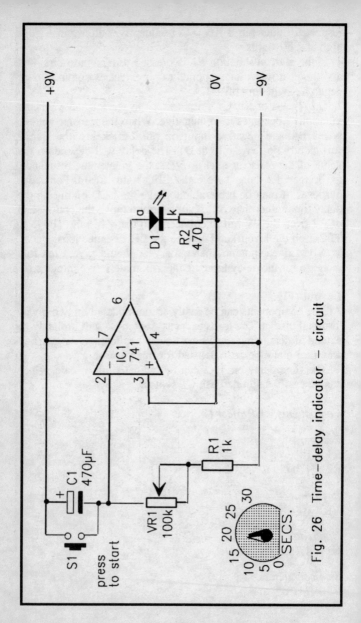

Fig. 26 Time-delay indicator — circuit

50

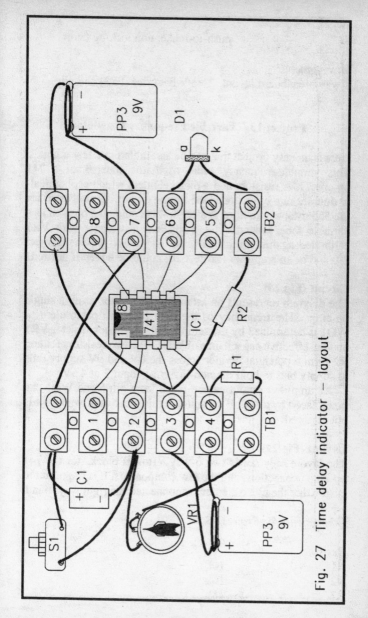

Fig. 27 Time delay indicator — layout

Switch
S1   push-to-make, non locking (start)

Miscellaneous
8-way breadboard layout, 2 × 9V batteries (PP3) and clip.

Project 13 – Variable Frequency Oscillator

Here is an easy project that can be assembled in a few minutes. This variable-frequency audio oscillator consists of a 741 op-amp, four resistors and a piezo element which economically doubles as a capacitor in the timing circuit. As suggested for the 555 astable circuit of Project 5, this could also be used as a variable tone generator for a musical instrument with VR1 calibrated against a musical scale. An octave divider (Project 29) and/or an amplifier (Project 26) could be added if desired.

Circuit (Fig.28)
The diagram represents an astable multivibrator using a single op-amp. The frequency of the tone from the piezo element WD1 is determined by the setting of the feedback resistor VR1 and the effective capacitance of WD1. The two resistors R1 and R2 form a potential divider across the 0V and 9V supply rails to supply bias to hold the non-inverting input 3 at 4.5V.

An amplifier output can be taken from pin 6 and WD1 can be replaced by a 100nF capacitor if this piezo audible output is not required.

Layout (Fig.29)
The layout only needs two 6-way terminal blocks for the 741 op-amp connections and the few components. It is important to ensure that the piezo element is connected the right way round.

Components for Project 13

Resistors
R1   10k
R2   10k
R3   18k

52

Potentiometer
VR1   1M (lin.)

Semiconductor
IC1   741 op-amp

Loudspeaker
WD1   piezo element

Switch
S1   S.P.S.T. (on/off)

Miscellaneous
8-way breadboard layout, 9V battery (PP3) and clip.

Project 14 – Mixer Preamplifier

Two 741 op-amps are needed for this two-stage audio mixer
and preamplifier. Several microphone, tape or radio sources can
be mixed by adding extra inputs. As these signal sources vary
in amplitude, some balancing will be required before the mixer
stage.

Circuit (Fig.30)

The circuit shows two inputs to pin 2 of IC1 via series resistors
R1 and R2. As mentioned, more input signals can be mixed via
additional series resistors. The 10k feedback resistor R4 limits
the gain of this mixer stage, and the output on pin 6 is routed
via electrolytic C1 and R5 in series to the inverting input (pin
2) of preamplifier IC2. Reducing the resistance of VR1 reduces
the gain of the preamplifier. The output can be applied to a
power amplifier such as the LM386 (see Project 26).

Layout (Fig.31)

As shown, two 8-way breadboard layouts are necessary, one for
each of the 741 op-amps. Alternatively, an 8-way and a 16-way
breadboard can be employed, making sure that the IC is
correctly wired to eight of the sixteen terminal screws. In this

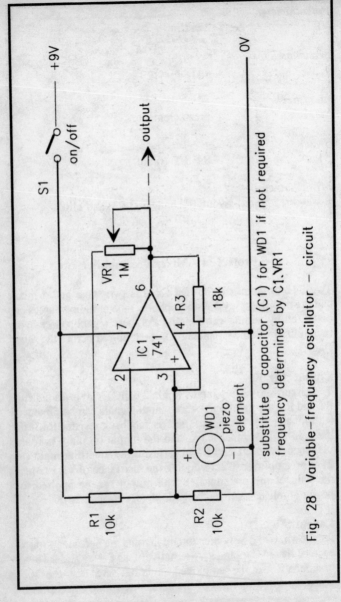

Fig. 28 Variable-frequency oscillator — circuit

substitute a capacitor (C1) for WD1 if not required
frequency determined by C1.VR1

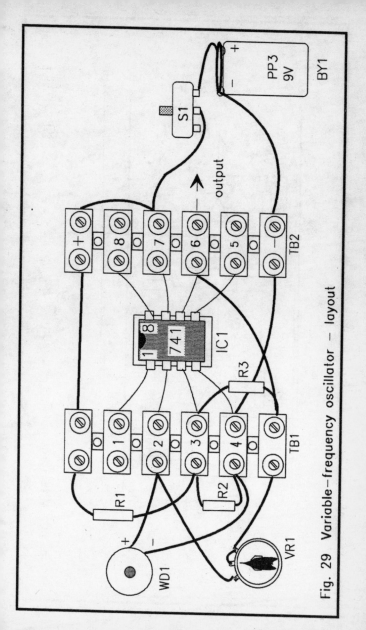

Fig. 29 Variable-frequency oscillator — layout

55

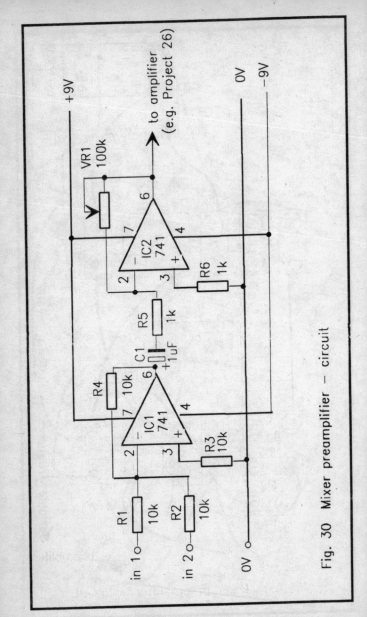

Fig. 30 Mixer preamplifier — circuit

56

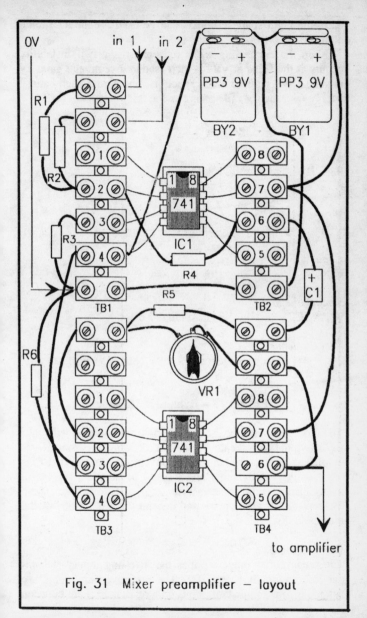

Fig. 31 Mixer preamplifier — layout

57

case, the eight spare terminals can be used for the additional connections.

Keep the connecting wires reasonably short; if instability occurs as the value of VR1 is increased to give greater gain, try adding two 0.1 microfarad capacitors, one across each battery supply with the 0V rail serving as the midpoint.

Components for Project 14

Resistors
R1 – R4   10k (4 off)
R5 & R6   1k (2 off)

Potentiometer
VR1   100k (lin

Capacitor
C1   1μF 10V elect.

Semiconductors
IC1 & IC2   741 op-amp (2 off)

Miscellaneous
2 × 8-way breadboard layouts, 2 × 9V batteries (PP3) and clip.

Project 15 – Dynamics Monitor

The dynamics monitor uses two 1458 dual op-amps with four LED outputs to indicate the degree of loudness from a pre-amplifier. Following musical convention, the four LEDs representing the dynamic levels could be labelled, piano (p), mezzo-piano (mp), mezzo-forte (mf) and forte (f). These dynamic levels are relative and depend upon the mood of the music.

Circuit (Fig.32)
The preamplifier input supplies the inverting inputs of comparator circuits IC1 and IC2. The non-inverting inputs are supplied from equidistant points on a resistance chain between

the +9V and 0V rails. Level adjustment is obtained by varying VR1 in series with fixed resistors R1 to R4. At low input levels, when the signal voltage (present on the inverting inputs) exceeds the chain voltage at IC2b pin 5, pin 7 will go negative and D4 (p) will light.

As the input signal increases, further comparators will switch over, until at loud signals, the chain voltage on IC1a pin 3 will be exceeded and D1 (f) will light in addition to the others. The setting of VR1 will determine the sensitivity between the steps; resistors R1 to R4 can also be varied to alter the degree of change between certain steps if required. Different colour LEDs can be used to distinguish between the levels, for instance a red LED for D1 could indicate the onset of overloading.

Layout (Fig.33)

The components again require two 8-way breadboard layouts, one for each of the 1458 dual op-amps. As in the previous project, a 16-way breadboard can also be pressed into service. If preferred, other op-amps can be used; for instance, four 741s or a single 339 quad op-amp. The pin numbers on the diagrams will of course need to be changed to suit these replacement op-amps.

Components for Project 15

Resistors

R1 – R4	10k (4 off)
R5 – R8	1k (4 off)

Potentiometer

VR1	100k (lin.)

Semiconductors

IC1 & IC2	1458 op-amp (2 off)
D1 – D4	LED (4 off, various colours)

Switch

S1	S.P.S.T. (on/off)

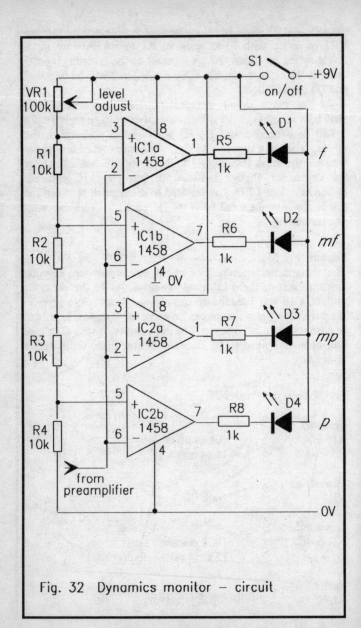

Fig. 32 Dynamics monitor — circuit

60

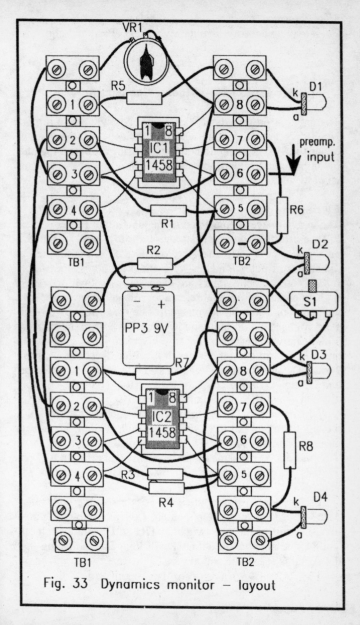

Fig. 33 Dynamics monitor – layout

61

2 × 8-way breadboard layouts, 9V battery (PP3) and clip.

Project 16 – Window Comparator

The previous project, the dynamics monitor, was also a form of window comparator – one with four panes if we continue the metaphor. This is a simpler comparator using a single 1458 dual op-amp that indicates when a signal is in or out of the selected window.

Circuit (Fig.34)

The input voltage is connected to the junction of IC1a pin3 and IC1b pin 6, the non-inverting and inverting input of the two op-amps respectively. The other inputs are each connected to the sliders of potentiometers VR1 and VR2 across the supply rails. These potentiometers are each set, as shown, to give a high reference and a low reference voltage input to the two comparators. If the input voltage lies between these two reference voltages, i.e. in the window, then the op-amp outputs are both negative. This occurs because inverting input 2 is positive and non-inverting input 5 is negative with respect to the signal. Diodes D4 and D5 do not conduct so TR1 remains switched off and D3 lights via the collector resistor R4. The light-emitting diodes D1 and D2 are also off.

If the input signal strays below the low reference set by VR2, the output on pin 7 of IC1b swings positive, diode D5 conducts and switches the base of TR1 into conduction; in turn, D3 is switched off. At the same time, the positive on the output of pin 7 lights D2 via R2, indicating that the signal is below the window.

Alternatively, if the input signal goes above the high reference setting (VR1), the output on pin 1 of IC1a will swing positive, D4 will conduct to switch on TR1 so D3 will switch off. Via R1, the positive on output 1 will light D1, indicating that the signal is above the window.

Layout (Fig.35)

The 8-way breadboard layout is shown in the diagram; two 8-way terminal blocks are adequate for the associated circuit components. As before, the layout can be modified to use two 741 op-amps if a 1458 is not available. Note that the pin numbers of the two types are not compatible.

Components for Project 16

Resistors

R1 & R2	1k (2 off)
R3	6.8k
R4	470 ohms

Potentiometers

VR1 & VR2	100k (lin.) (2 off)

Semiconductors

IC1	1458 op-amp (or two 741s)
TR1	BC109
D1 – D3	LED (3 off, different colours)
D4 & D5	1N4148 diodes (2 off)

Switch

S1	S.P.S.T. (on/off)

Miscellaneous

8-way breadboard layout, 9V battery (PP3) and clip.

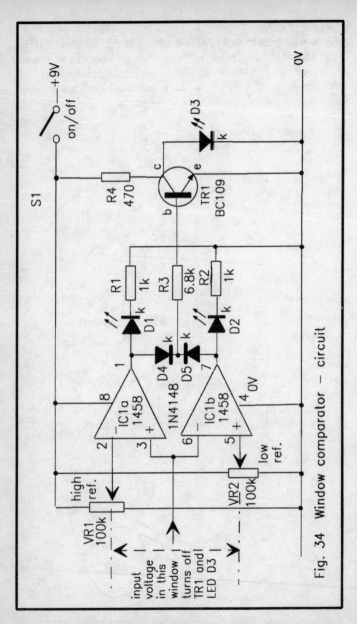

Fig. 34 Window comparator – circuit

64

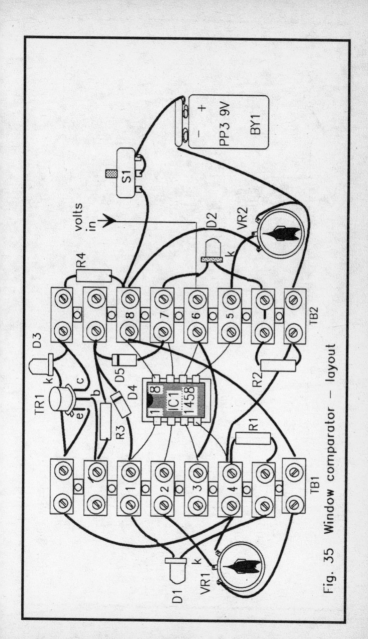

Fig. 35 Window comparator — layout

Chapter 4

COUNTER PROJECTS

Electronic counter chips suggest some interesting projects, particularly with flashing lights. Here is a visual metronome, a dice and a few board games that indicate some of the possibilities. The popular 4017 decade counter/divider chip forms the basis of these projects. Most of these counter projects need a clock generator, or a trigger input to step through the decade output stages. You will no doubt recognise that some of the earlier 555 projects have been adapted to pulse the counter. There is no reason why two of these projects cannot be combined in modular fashion.

Project 17 – Bar Counter Metronome

This visual metronome uses from two to four flashing LEDs depending on the time signature of the particular piece of music you happen to be singing, playing or perhaps conducting. The time signature at the beginning of a section of music consists of two numbers, one over the other like a fraction. Often the lower number is 4, which means that the basic beats are quarter notes (crochets) in a bar of music. The upper number is often 2, 3, or 4, denoting the number of these beats in a bar. So in simple time, we have two-four time (two crochet beats to the bar), three-four time (three crochet beats to the bar), and four-four time (four crochet beats to the bar). It therefore seems useful to have a metronome that will show you the number of beats in the bar, for it is easy for music students to miss a note and be on a down-beat when they should be on an up-beat or vice versa.

Circuit (Fig.36)
Basically, the circuit consists of a 555 pulse generator used to clock a 4017 counter. The speed of the clock pulses, the tempo, is controlled by VR1, a variable resistor through which the timing capacitor C1 charges. The rectangular output pulses on IC1, pin 3, are connected directly to input pin 14 on counter IC2. For

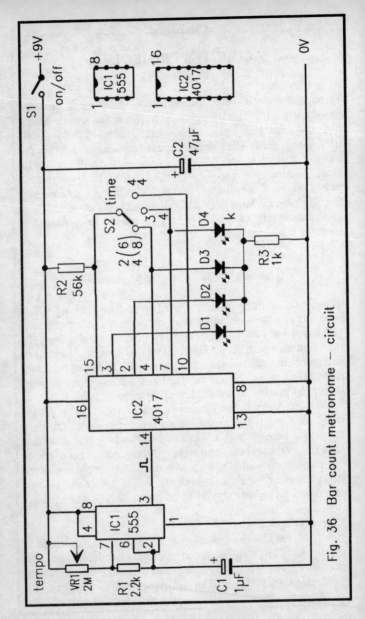

Fig. 36 Bar count metronome – circuit

68

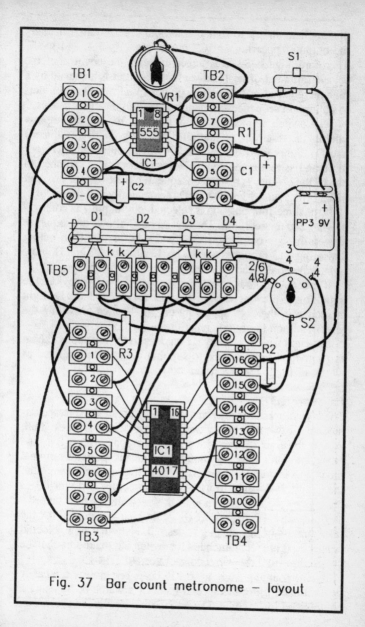

Fig. 37 Bar count metronome — layout

69

this application, up to four outputs only are required, namely the outputs appearing on IC2 pin 3, pin 2, pin 4, and pin 7. Therefore, switch S2 is arranged to reset the count after the selected number of beats have elapsed. Reset is achieved by a high on pin 15. Normally, a low on pin 15 allows all ten outputs to go high in sequence in synchronism with the clock pulses.

With switch S2 in the two-four position, the low on output 4 inhibits the reset pin. Output pins 3 and 2 go high in sequence and D1 lights followed by D2. However, output 4 now goes high, and as this is the condition for reset, as it is switched to pin 15 the counter is reset. Consequently, the two-four position of S2 brings on D1 and D2 LEDs sequentially and repeatedly.

If the three-four position is selected, output pin 7 is connected via S2 to the reset pin. The low on pin 7 allows the sequence to step through output pins 3, 2 and 4 before the high output appearing on 7 produces a reset, i.e. LEDs, D1, D2 and D3 now light sequentially and repeatedly.

If four-four time is selected, then output pin 10 provides the initial low to prevent reset. In this case D1, D2, D3 and D4 light in sequence, the high appearing on pin 10 then providing the reset condition to provide repetition.

Six-eight time is actually six quavers to the bar and is known as compound time; suffice to say that it can be considered as two beats to the bar at a faster tempo.

Layout (Fig.37)

The layout uses an 8-way and a 16-way breadboard to accommodate the two ICs. In addition, an 8-way terminal block, TB5, groups the four LEDs, which can be mounted on a five-line music stave for effect. Although this means an extra terminal block, this is preferable to wiring the LEDs haphazardly around the circuit. It is better to use a different colour LED for D1 to distinguish the first beat in the bar, which should be accented.

A separate TB for the LEDs could also be adopted for the later circuits in this chapter if desired. Note that four soldered connections are recommended for switch S2; make sure that the connection from the wiper contact goes to TB4-15.

A scale ranging from 44 to 156 beats per minute can easily be calibrated using the second hand of a watch or by using a commercial metronome. The tempo marks given on the music, such as andante, allegro, vivace, etc., can also be added to the scale.

Components for Project 17

Resistors

R1	2.2k
R2	56k
R3	1k

Potentiometer

VR1	2M (lin.)

Capacitors

C1	1µF 10V elect.
C2	47µF 10V elect.

Semiconductors

IC1	NE555 timer
IC2	4017 decade counter/divider
D1 – D4	LED (4 off)

Switch

S1	S.P.S.T. (on/off)

Miscellaneous

8-way breadboard layout, 9V battery (PP3) and clip.
18-way breadboard layout, additional terminal block.

Project 18 – Electronic Dice

This electronic dice gives a random selection of six numbers at the touch of a button. Strictly speaking, the only advantages over the conventional die or dice is that it is not easily lost, does not roll off the table, requires less physical energy to display a number and looks more impressive.

71

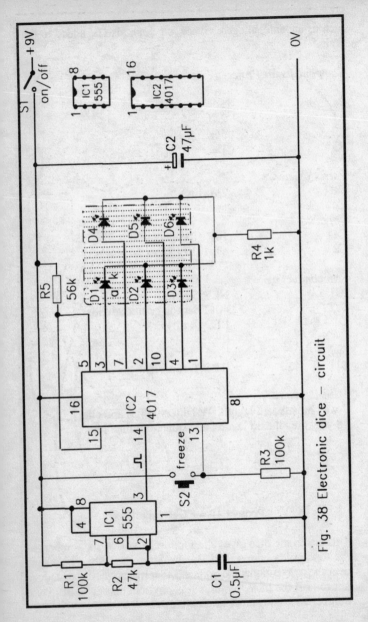

Fig. 38 Electronic dice — circuit

72

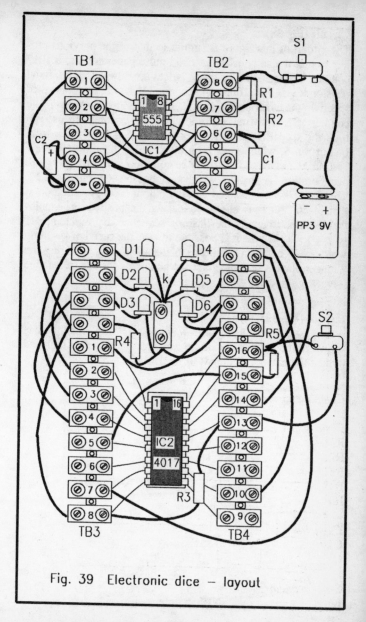

Fig. 39 Electronic dice — layout

73

Circuit (Fig.38)

The circuit of this figure is similar to that of the previous project in that it also consists of a 555 pulse generator and a 4017 counter. The speed of the clock pulses are now set with a fixed resistor R1 and the timing capacitor C1 has been reduced to speed up the clock pulses on IC1, pin 3 feeding input pin 14 on counter IC2. The first six outputs of the counter are used to light the six LEDs and the reset on pin 15 is now taken from output pin 5, which goes high after the sixth output. The six LEDs, D1 to D6, run in sequence continuously until the freeze pushbutton S2 is pressed, which switches the +9V rail to pin 13. The clock is then disabled and the output LED switched on at that instant remains alight. Releasing the pushbutton enables the clock and restarts the flashing sequence. By replacing R1 with a 100k variable it is possible to vary the speed of flashing, which may be a useful means of handicapping or aiding the younger players in some games to anticipate the run of the dice – loading the dice!

Layout (Fig.39)

A suggested layout using an 8-way and a 16-way breadboard is shown in the diagram. A single-way terminal block is included to take the cathode (k) leads of the LEDs.

Components for Project 18

Resistors

R1	100k
R2	47k
R3	100k
R4	1k
R5	56k

Capacitors

C1	0.5µF
C2	47µF 10V elect.

Semiconductors

IC1	NE555 timer

| IC2 | 4017 decade counter/divider |
| D1 – D6 | LED (6 off) |

Switches

| S1 | S.P.S.T. (on/off) |
| S2 | push-to-make, non-locking (freeze) |

Miscellaneous

8-way and 16-way breadboard layouts, 9V battery (PP3) and clip.

Project 19 – Red LED/Green LED Game

This game is an extension of the last project, the electronic dice. It gives a random selection of ten outputs making use of the green and red glows produced by five tri-colour LEDs. Press a freeze pushbutton and one of the five LEDs will remain on. But which one? Will it be green or will it be red? It's a good basis for a board game, and if the clock pulses are slowed down there is added skill in anticipating which LED will be displayed and which colour. A suggested method of numbering the output LEDs, green 1–5 and red 1–5, is shown in Figure 44. Coloured lettering would be even more attractive.

Circuit (Fig.40)

The pulse generator IC1 is identical to the circuit for the electronic dice project. The counter stage IC2 includes the freeze switch S2 to disable the clock to select an output LED for display. However, as all ten outputs need to be stepped continuously, the reset, pin 15, is taken directly to the 0V line. The outputs are arranged so that the colour sequence of the LEDs alternates between red and green.

Layout (Fig.41)

From the diagram it can be seen that the 8-way breadboard layout is identical to the previous project. The 16-way breadboard wiring needs a little care especially when positioning the five tri-colour LEDs. Extra terminal blocks and some sleeving may be necessary to avoid short-circuits.

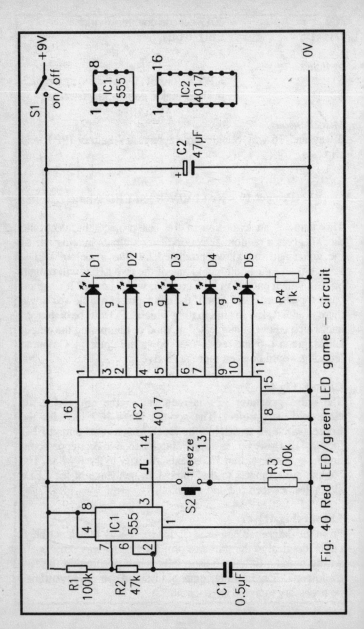

Fig. 40 Red LED/green LED game — circuit

76

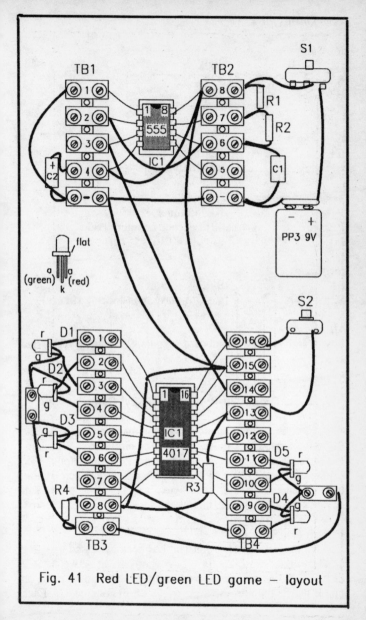

Fig. 41 Red LED/green LED game — layout

77

Resistors

R1	100k
R2	47k
R3	100k
R4	1k

Capacitors

C1	0.5µF
C2	47µF 10V elect.

Semiconductors

IC1	NE555 timer
IC2	4017 decade counter/divider
D1 – D5	tri-colour LEDs (5 off)

Switches

S1	S.P.S.T. (on/off)
S2	push-to-make, non-locking (freeze)

Miscellaneous
8-way and 16-way breadboard layouts, 9V battery (PP3) and clip.

Project 20 – 'Trigger Happy' Game

The previous counter circuits have used the astable mode of the 555 to generate clock pulses. This game circuit uses the mono-stable mode to trigger the counter and step the outputs. The trigger input could be a switch contact, a light gun activating a light-dependent resistor, etc. Each trigger input pulse will advance the LED decade output and indicate a player's score.

Circuit (Fig.42)
For this project, the time constant has been increased by using an electrolytic capacitor for C1. A short-circuit between pin 2 of IC1 and 0V produces a fixed length positive-going pulse on pin 3, which supplies the input to pin 14 of counter IC2. Each

trigger input steps the positive output of IC2 on to light the LEDs one by one in an alternating colour sequence. Note that the clock enable, pin 13, is now connected to the 0V rail. Apart from this, the wiring for the counter, IC2, is identical to the previous project.

Layout (Fig.43)
The layout differs slightly from the previous project, mainly in the 8-way breadboard section. Again, extra terminal blocks and some sleeving may be necessary to avoid short-circuits when wiring the tri-colour LEDs.

Components for Project 20

Resistors

R1	100k
R2	5.6k
R3	1k

Capacitors

C1	4.7µF 10V elect.
C2	47µF 10V elect.

Semiconductors

IC1	NE555 timer
IC2	4017 decade counter/divider
D1 – D5	tri-colour LEDs (5 off)

Switch

S1	S.P.S.T. (on/off)

Miscellaneous
8-way and 16-way breadboard layouts, 9V battery (PP3) and clip.

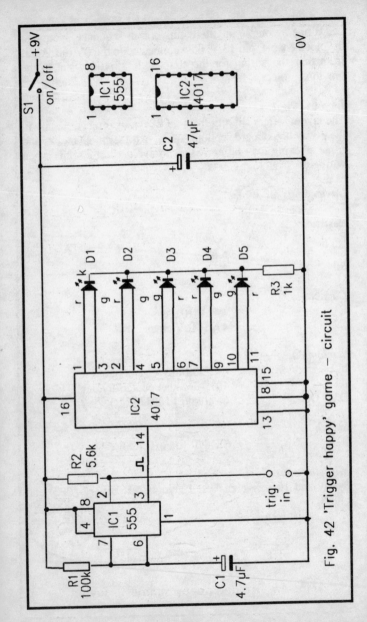

Fig. 42 'Trigger happy' game – circuit

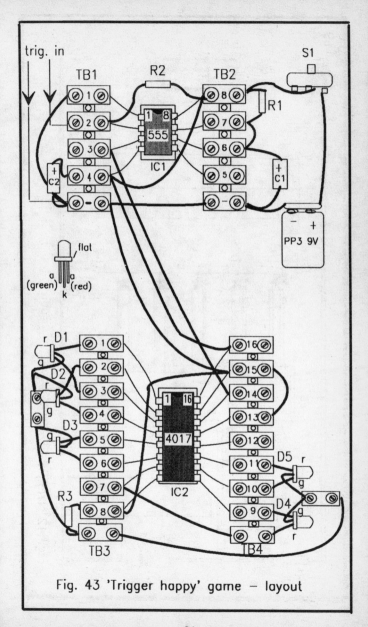

Fig. 43 'Trigger happy' game — layout

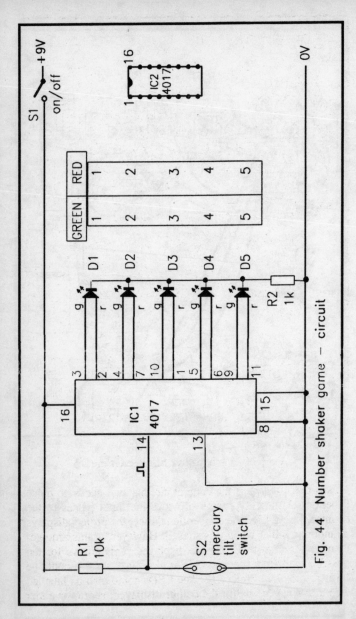

Fig. 44 Number shaker game – circuit

82

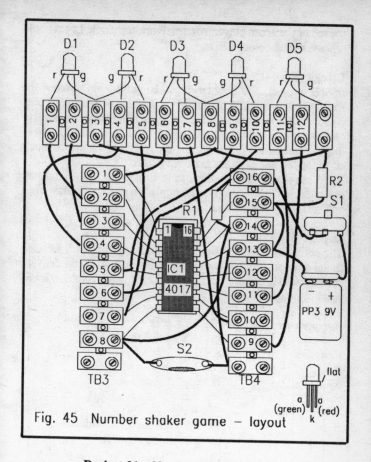

Fig. 45 Number shaker game – layout

Project 21 – Number Shaker Game

This is the simplest of the counter circuits as it needs no pulse generator. A mercury switch provides the input pulses to the counter circuit. Like the conventional dice, the project displays a random number when it is shaken. However, in this arrangement five red/green LEDs are displayed. This allows for ten possible numbers or letters, but for dice purposes this could be limited to 6 as in Project 18. The LEDs could also be labelled 1 to 5 and depending on the colour displayed, score for either the red or the green player. Alternatively, ten single LEDs could replace the tri-colour LEDs.

Circuit (Fig.44)

In this project, the counter input is pulsed by shaking the mercury tilt switch S2, which gives a series of negative-going pulses to IC1 input pin 14. Each trigger input provides positive output steps to light the LEDs one by one in succession. Note that the clock enable, pin 13, and the reset, pin 15, are connected to the 0V rail as in the previous project.

To use the circuit as a dice, as in Project 18, pin 15 must be disconnected from the 0V rail, coupled to pin 5 and taken via a 56k resistor to the +9V rail.

Layout (Fig.45)

The layout uses the 16-way breadboard, together with an additional terminal block to mount the LEDs in line. Some sleeving on the cathode (centre lead) of the LEDs is advisable to avoid short-circuits.

Components for Project 21

Resistors
R1   10k
R2   1k

Semiconductors
IC1   4017 decade counter/divider
D1 – D5   tri-colour LEDs (5 off)

Switches
S1   S.P.S.T. (on/off)
S2   mercury tilt

Miscellaneous
16-way breadboard layout, 9V battery (PP3) and clip, additional 12-way terminal block.

Chapter 5

NAND-GATE PROJECTS

The projects in this chapter nearly all use inverters made from the CMOS 4011 quad two-input NAND-gate with its inputs linked together. This IC is mounted on the 14-way breadboard. Not all of the four gates are used for some of the projects and unused gates have their inputs linked to the 0V rail to prevent power wastage due to stray pick up. With so many redundant pins, spare terminals on TB1 and TB2 can be acquired and wiring reduced by linking any common input pin leads to one terminal, instead of following the layout diagrams given. However, do remember to revert to the original layout when input pins are not required to be linked, e.g. for Projects 23 and 25.

Project 22 – Touch/Moisture Detector

This touch switch finds application in security systems where touching an innocent-looking metal surface sounds an alarm or lights a warning light. It can also be used to indicate that it's starting to rain, a tank is about to overflow, etc. The sensing plates can be two adjacent metal objects or two strips of a printed-circuit board.

Circuit (Fig.46)

The touch circuit basically comprises IC1a, IC1b, two gates of a 4011 forming a Schmitt trigger, and a transistor output stage, TR1. When a contact is made across the sensing plates, inputs 1 and 2 of inverter IC1a go high and the output on pin 3 goes low. This low is fed via inverter IC1b to produce a high output on pin 4. Via its base resistor R3, transistor TR1 switches on and the collector current causes LED D1 to light via the limiting resistor R4. The high value resistor R2 provides a small amount of feedback to make the switching action more positive.

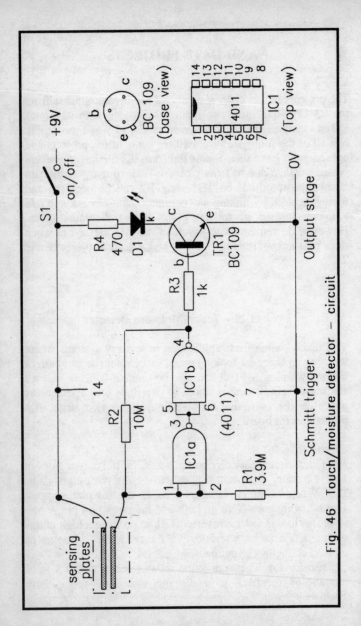

Fig. 46 Touch/moisture detector – circuit

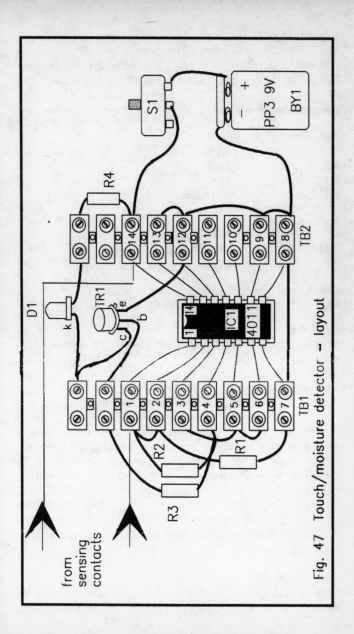

Fig. 47 Touch/moisture detector – layout

87

Layout (Fig.47)
The layout diagram indicates the connections for the sensing contacts. A length of twin cable is suitable for this purpose. Check that the connections of D1 and TR1 are as shown.

Components for Project 22

Resistors
R1	3.9M
R2	10M
R3	1k
R4	470 ohms

Semiconductors
IC1	4011 NAND-gate
TR1	BC109
D1	LED

Switch
S1	S.P.S.T. (on/off)

Miscellaneous
Sensing plates, 14-way breadboard layout, 9V battery (PP3) and clip.

Project 23 – Precedence Indicator

If you watch TV quiz games then you will have seen contestants frantically thumping precedence switches to claim the right to answer. Press it first and your light comes on to the exclusion of your opponents. If push-to-make non-locking switches are used, then it is necessary for contestants to hold the pushbuttons pressed until the winner has been established, otherwise an opponent could capture the light. If locking pushbuttons are preferred, they must be released to restart after every question.

Circuit (Fig.48)
Only two gates, wired as inverters, are required for this bistable circuit. With no pushbuttons pressed, the inputs of both

inverters are held high via R1 and R4 connected to the +9V rail. This produces low outputs at pin 3 and pin 4, so both LEDs are off. If we assume that pushbutton S1 is pressed first, the input of IC1a will go low because it is coupled to the low on pin 4. Therefore, the output of IC1a goes high and D1 lights. Pressing S2 will now have no effect because the high on pin 3 transferred to pins 5 and 6 maintains the inverters in their present state. Similarly, if S2 is pressed first, then D2 lights and D1 is inhibited.

Layout (Fig.49)

The few components fit comfortably on the 14-way breadboard, which must be sited in front of the quiz controller. Remember to link the inputs of the spare gates to the 0V rail on TB2. Different colours should be used for each of the two LEDs to enable the player who is first off the mark to be identified. The players' pushbutton switches S1 and S2 should be connected by lengths of flex to allow adequate space between them and the quiz controller. Ideally, each pushbutton should be mounted on a solid base and colour-coded to correspond with the LEDs.

Components for Project 23

Resistors
R1 & R4	3.9M (2 off)
R2 & R3	680 ohms (2 off)

Semiconductors
IC1	4011 NAND-gate
D1	LED (green)
D2	LED (red)

Switches
S1, S2	push-to-make (see text)
S3	S.P.S.T. (on/off)

Miscellaneous
14-way breadboard layout, 9V battery (PP3) and clip.

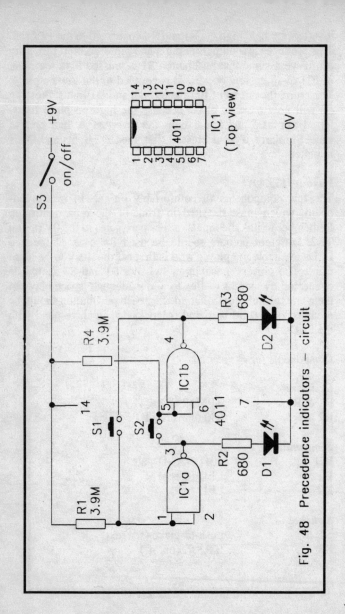

Fig. 48 Precedence indicators – circuit

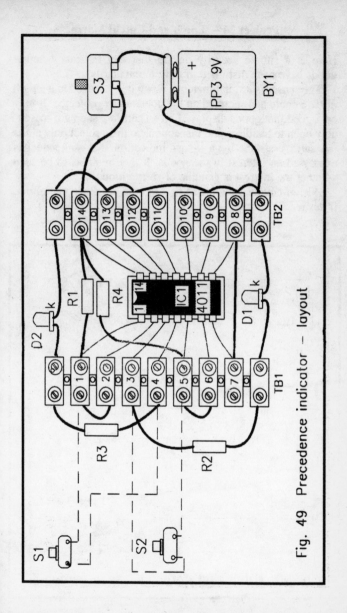

Fig. 49 Precedence indicator — layout

Project 24 – 'Latch and Catch' Alarm

Here is a simple security device that can indicate whether goods have been disturbed, if only momentarily.

The sensor is a small mercury tilt switch attached to a length of twin cable and secreted on the goods to be protected. It may be argued that goods displayed on a shelf in a shop are reasonably open to handling and inspection, so this project only alerts the sales assistant by a visual indication that someone has expressed an interest in the goods. It then remains to be seen whether the interest is genuine or surreptitious.

It is, of course, possible to fit a remote buzzer to the output, if desired.

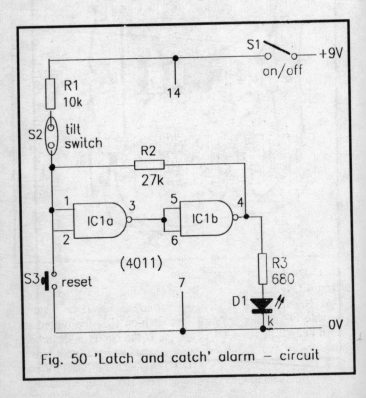

Fig. 50 'Latch and catch' alarm – circuit

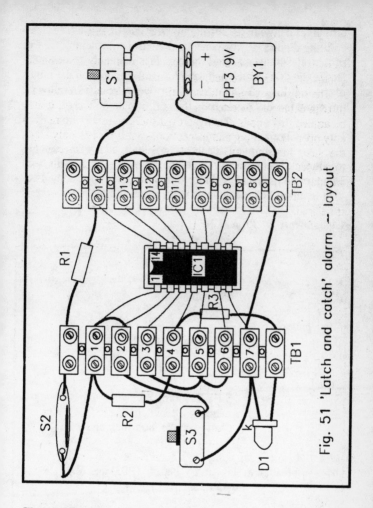

Fig. 51 'Latch and catch' alarm – layout

Circuit (Fig.50)

Two NAND-gates IC1a–IC1b wired as inverters form a bistable or flip-flop circuit. At switch-on (S1) the output on IC1b pin 4 is low, so D1 is not on. If the circuit is disturbed, mercury tilt switch S2 will make contact and the input pins 1 and 2 of IC1a will go high via R1 connected to the +9V rail. This results in a low on the output of the first inverter, which in turn gives a high to the second inverter output, pin 4. The light-emitting diode D1 is activated and latches on, catching the eye of the sales assistant, until the circuit is manually reset by S3. Hence the title, 'Latch and catch' alarm! The low on the inputs of the first inverter when 'reset' is pressed, results in a low on pin 4 and the LED switches off.

Layout (Fig.51)

The layout is simplicity itself and will only take a few minutes to connect. In a practical situation, the tilt switch S2 will be at some remote sensing position. A length of twin flex and a two-way terminal block can be used for extension purposes.

Components for Project 24

Resistors

R1	10k
R2	27k
R3	680 ohms

Semiconductors

IC1	4011 NAND-gate
D1	LED

Switches

S1	S.P.S.T. (on/off)
S2	mercury tilt switch
S3	push-to-make, non-locking (reset)

Miscellaneous
14-way breadboard layout, 9V battery (PP3) and clip.

Project 25 – Pulsed-Tone Alarm

For alarm systems, a pulsed intermittent tone is often more effective than a continuous one. Here is an alarm using a 4011 NAND-gate IC that gives a 1kHz tone at approximately one second intervals when the battery voltage is applied. The on/off switch contacts can be used as a sensor or, for instance, a reed switch operated by a magnet in a window, or door frame.

Circuit (Fig.52)

All four gates are used in this circuit, IC1a – IC1b forming the low-frequency 1Hz astable, IC1c – IC1d forming the higher audio-frequency 1kHz astable. Other frequencies for the two oscillators may be selected by changing the values of the timing components: R1, C1, and R2, C2.

The 1Hz output pulses from IC1b are coupled to input 9 of IC1c to enable the audio oscillator IC1c – IC1d, once per second, when the low-frequency pulses from the first astable are high. The output signal from IC1d pin 11 is applied via R3 to the base of the output transistor TR1, to energise LS1 in the collector circuit.

Layout (Fig.53)

Although the circuit diagram looks busy, the layout on the 14-way breadboard requires few components and is surprisingly uncluttered; a reminder that the integrated circuit takes care of most of the components.

Components for Project 25

Resistors
R1   10M
R2 & R3   47k (2 off)

Capacitors
C1 & C2   47nF (2 off)
C3   100μF 10V elect.

Loudspeaker
LS1   64 ohms

Semiconductors
IC1   4011 NAND-gate
TR1   BC109

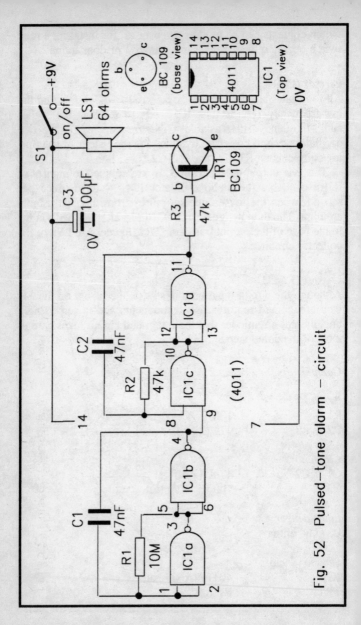

Fig. 52 Pulsed-tone alarm — circuit

96

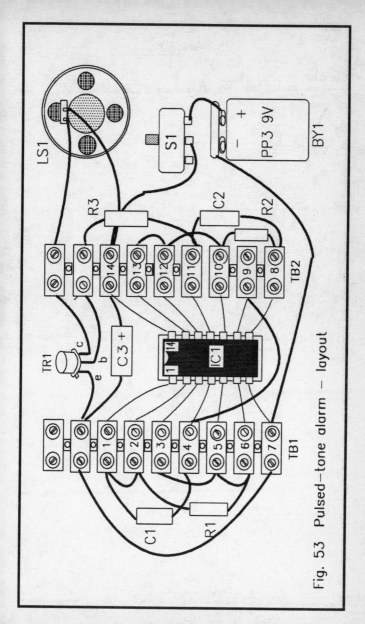

Fig. 53 Pulsed-tone alarm – layout

97

Switch
S1   S.P.S.T. (on/off)

Miscellaneous
14-way breadboard layout, 9V battery (PP3) and clip.

Chapter 6

MISCELLANEOUS PROJECTS

The previous chapters have each centred around one particular type of chip so that a variety of projects could be constructed with the minimum of components. Although three different ICs are required to complete all the projects in this last chapter, three of the projects can be built around the LM386 amplifier. Finally, two remaining musical projects require a 4013 divider and a 4051 b.c.d. decoder. These projects can be combined with others to make an unusual musical instrument.

Project 26 – General Purpose Amplifier

A compact, battery-operated amplifier has a variety of uses in project building to boost small signal outputs. This general-purpose audio amplifier is based around the popular LM386 8-pin integrated circuit.

Normally, the amplifier has a voltage gain of 20, but external components can be added to obtain gains of up to 200.

Circuit (Fig.54)

As shown, the basic amplifier circuit uses few components. The input signal can be controlled by the potentiometer VR1 and applied via the wiper to the amplifier input pin 2. As stated, the voltage gain is internally fixed to 20 but can be increased by adding a component network between pins 1 and 8. A 1.2k resistor in series with a 10μF capacitor (+ terminal to pin 1) between these pins increases the gain to about 50. Reducing this resistor further increases the gain, and when bridged by the capacitor alone gives a gain of about 200.

The output on pin 5 is applied via C2 to LS1. A larger speaker mounted on a baffle will help to improve the lower audio response; an 8-ohm impedance is suitable. Capacitor C1 prevents instability on the supply line. The input leads should be kept as short as possible, and the voltage gain reduced if there is any tendency to instability.

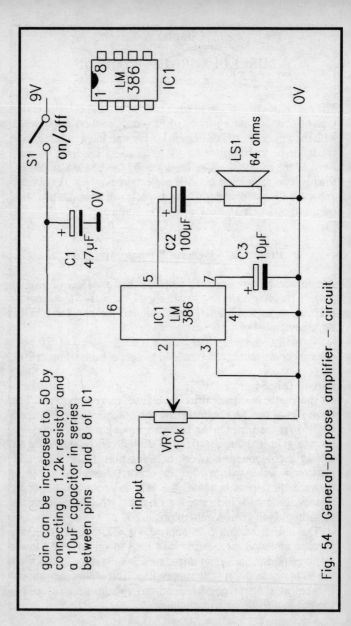

gain can be increased to 50 by
connecting a 1.2k resistor and
a 10uF capacitor in series
between pins 1 and 8 of IC1

Fig. 54 General-purpose amplifier – circuit

100

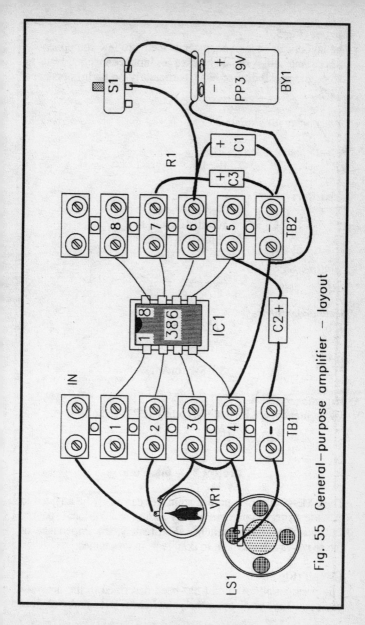

Fig. 55 General-purpose amplifier – layout

101

Layout (Fig.55)

The layout can be kept compact as there are few components.

Screened cables should be used for input connecting leads to reduce the possibility of hum, particularly on high impedance inputs.

Components for Project 26

Potentiometer
VR1   10k lin.

Capacitors
C1   47µF 10V elect.
C2   100µF 10V elect.
C3   10µF 10V elect.

Loudspeaker
LS1   (see text)

Semiconductor
IC1   LM386 amplifier

Switch
S1   S.P.S.T (on/off)

Miscellaneous
8-way breadboard layout, 9V battery (PP3) and clip.

Project 27 – Intercom

The LM386 general-purpose amplifier can easily be adapted to provide a simple intercom link by adding an additional speaker and two changeover switches. Fortunately, the impedance of the speakers allows them to double as microphones.

Circuit (Fig.56)

The basic amplifier circuit has been described in the previous project. The two operator's switches, S1 and S2, are changeover switches, preferably of the non-locking type. Two single-pole double-throw microswitches are suitable, wired in the push-to-talk mode. In the circuit diagram, S1 is shown operated. Consequently, the loudspeaker, LS1, on the main unit is switched by S1 as a microphone, i.e. in the talk position. The input from LS1 is controlled in volume by VR1 and amplified by IC1. The output on pin 5 is coupled via C2 and applied over the link to the listen position of S2 and loudspeaker LS2. When S1 is released, the operator at the remote station can reply by pressing S2 to the talk position. The voltage gain of the amplifier can be increased as necessary, as explained in the previous project. When testing the intercom, keep the loudspeakers some distance away from each other to avoid acoustic feedback between them, i.e. the output from the loudspeaker feeding back into the microphone resulting in 'howling'.

No method of calling is used other than speaking into the microphone. Where this proves difficult because of ambient noise, a signal source, from the pulsed-tone alarm of Project 25, for example, could be capactively coupled to VR1 as both stations are normally in the listening mode. Extra switching arrangements would, of course, be required.

Layout (Fig.57)
The main unit layout is shown on an 8-way breadboard with the three connections that link to the remote switch S2 and speaker/microphone LS2. The layout can be kept compact as there are few components.

Components for Project 27

Potentiometer
VR1   10k lin.

Capacitors
C1   47µF 10V elect.
C2   100µF 10V elect.
C3   10µF 10V elect.

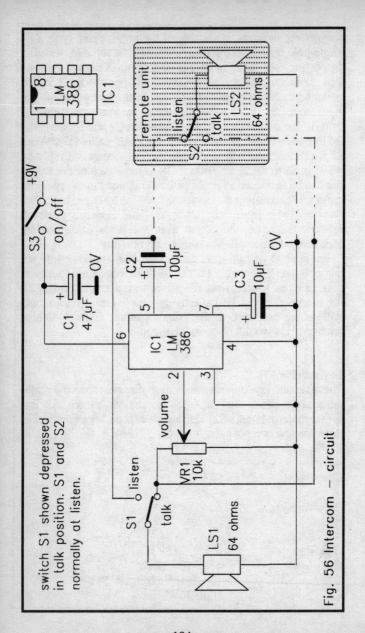

Fig. 56 Intercom – circuit

104

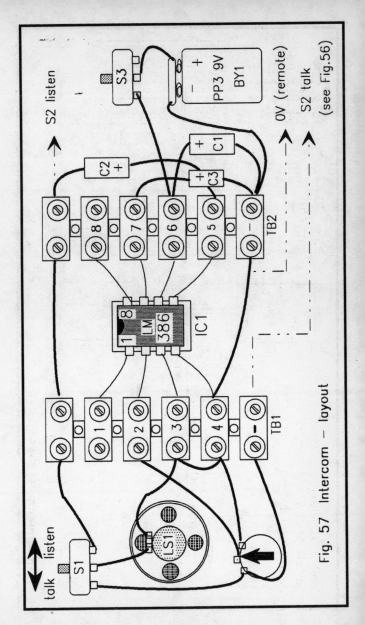

Fig. 57 Intercom — layout

105

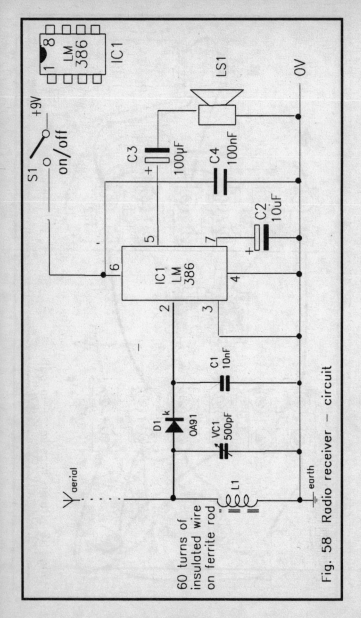

Fig. 58 Radio receiver – circuit

106

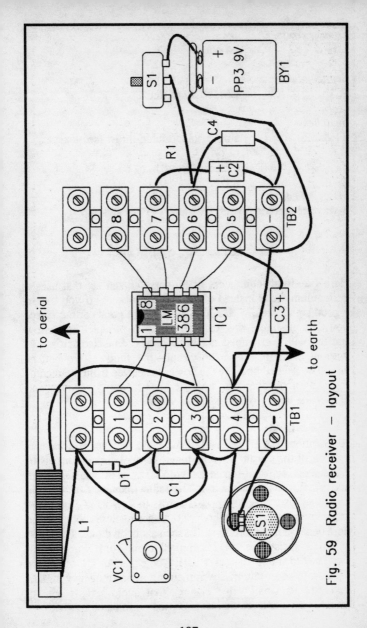

Fig. 59 Radio receiver – layout

107

Loudspeakers
LS1 & LS2   64 ohms (2 off)

Semiconductor
IC1   LM386 amplifier

Switches
S1 & S2   single-pole, double-throw (see text)
                           (2 off)
S3   S.P.S.T. (on/off)

Miscellaneous
8-way breadboard layout, 9V battery (PP3) and clip.

Project 28 – Radio Receiver

Here's a circuit equivalent of an early crystal set that uses a germanium diode instead of the 'cat's whisker'. If you live in a good signal area, with a high aerial and a good earth connection, it's an interesting experiment to try to pick up a few stations with high impedance headphones connected across C1, without using IC1 and the circuit that follows. No battery would be needed because the power is derived from the incoming station. Adding the amplifier is of course a bonus and allows the luxury of loudspeaker volume.

Circuit (Fig.58)

As mentioned, the front-end of the radio receiver is a modern version of the crystal set. The tuned parallel circuit consists of L1, a short length of ferrite rod with 60 turns of insulated wire, and VC1, a tuning capacitor. The radio frequency (r.f.) signal picked up by the aerial appears across this resonant circuit and is rectified by the signal diode, D1. A germanium diode is used here because it is more sensitive than a silicon diode. The audio signal at the cathode of D1 is applied to pin 2 of IC1 and amplified to feed the loudspeaker LS1. The capacitor C1 acts as an r.f. trap to short-circuit any remaining radio frequency signals to earth. Its small value ensures that audio signals are not affected by it and are therefore passed on to the amplifier.

The main problem with such a simple circuit is that other strong signals may break through because the single tuned circuit does not give sufficient discrimination.

Layout (Fig.59)
The variable tuning capacitor C1 will probably have two solder tags for attaching the leads. Preferably, these should be soldered, but alternatively they could be wire-wrapped. The ends of the inductor coil L1 can be secured on the ferrite rod with a dab of wax or a strip of adhesive tape. Make sure that the ends of the wires are scraped clean to make good connection in the terminal block. The aerial wire should be as high as possible and the earth lead firmly secured to a copper rod in the ground or to a cold water-pipe.

Components for Project 28

Capacitors
C1	10nF
C2	10µF 10V elect.
C3	100µF 10V elect.
C4	100nF
VC1	500pF variable (tuning)

Inductance
L1	60 turns of fine insulated wire on ferrite rod

Loudspeaker
LS1	64 ohms

Semiconductors
IC1	LM386 amplifier
D1	OA91 germanium diode

Switch
S1	S.P.S.T. (on/off)

Miscellaneous
8-way breadboard layout, 9V battery (PP3) and clip.

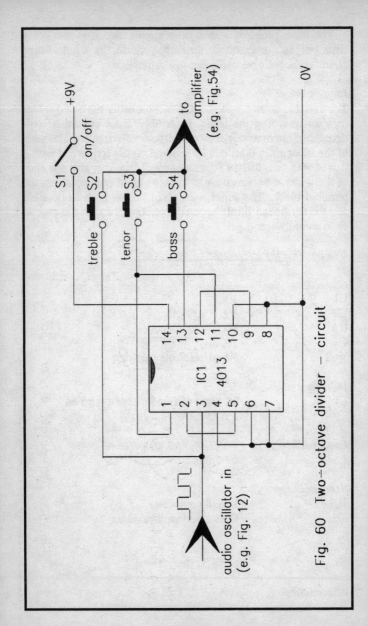

Fig. 60 Two-octave divider – circuit

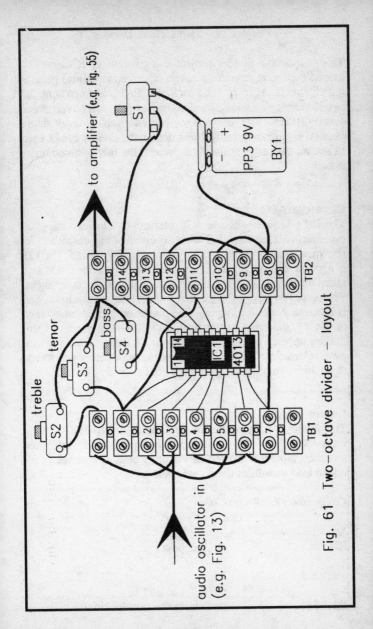

Fig. 61 Two-octave divider — layout

Project 29 – Two Octave Divider

This two-octave divider project using the 4013 IC serves to extend the lower range of a single-note (monophonic) generator, electronic organ or audio oscillator. In this arrangement, the two divider circuits can be switched to give effectively three octave voices: with dividers by-passed (treble), used singly (tenor), or cascaded (bass). In particular, the divider can be used to extend the range of the final project, the three-valve music-maker.

Circuit (Fig.60)

The 4013 frequency divider IC1 produces two lower octaves by dividing by 2, and by 4 if the two dividers are cascaded. As shown, a signal from an audio oscillator (e.g. Project 5, Fig.12), is applied to input pin 3, the input of the first divider. It is also taken directly to switch S2 (treble) to give a top octave output. The output on pin 1 from the first divider is an octave lower and is taken to switch S3 (tenor). The output on pin 1 is also taken to pin 11, the input of the second divider. The output of this divider appears on pin 13 is taken to S4 (bass). All three outputs, selected by S2, S3, or S4, are coupled together and routed to an audio amplifier (e.g. Project 26, Fig.54).

Layout (Fig.61)

This layout is perhaps the simplest as, apart from the 4013 IC, it consists of only the power input circuit and three pushbutton switches. Note that connections to other circuits also need a 0V return lead as well as the signal lead.

Components for Project 29

Semiconductor
IC1   4013 divider

Switches
S1   S.P.S.T. (on/off)
S2 – S4   push-to-make, non-locking (3 off)

14-way breadboard layout, 9V battery (PP3) and clip.

Project 30 – Three Valve Music-maker

Here's a title for a project that sounds like an old radio set, but is in fact the basis of a novel musical instrument that can play up to eight different notes. The 'three-valve' description refers to the trio of switches that emulates the valve action of a trumpet. The circuit lends itself to some interesting adaptations. Here, three pushbuttons are used in a one-to-eight analogue multiplexer circuit (4051) to select eight timing resistors to tune an audio oscillator, e.g. the astable of Project 5. The combination of three switches enables the eight different notes, which conveniently allows all the notes in a diatonic scale – no flats, no sharps – to be played.

Variations on a Theme
Alternatively, like the trumpet, the notes could be arranged in steps of a semitone (chromatically), by choice of resistors, to cover part of the scale. The trumpet player merely extends the range by varying lip tension; in this version, the range could be extended by switching in an octave divider.

The three switches manually provide a binary code, but a pre-selected sequence of notes can be arranged to play automatically by replacing the switches with a BCD counter. As mentioned, the three switches give the possibility of eight combinations (resistors R1 to R8 can each give a different note if desired), one more than available with the three valves on a trumpet, which adds different tube lengths.

Circuit (Fig.62)
The basic circuit diagram shows the 4051 one-to-eight analogue switch IC1, and the associated components. Resistors R1 to R8 are individually selected by a combination of the note select keys S1 to S3. The chosen resistor value is routed to output pin 3 of IC1 when the attack key S4 is pressed. In turn, this output pin connects the resistor to the timing circuit of an audio oscillator, for example, the astable circuit of Project 5, Fig.12.

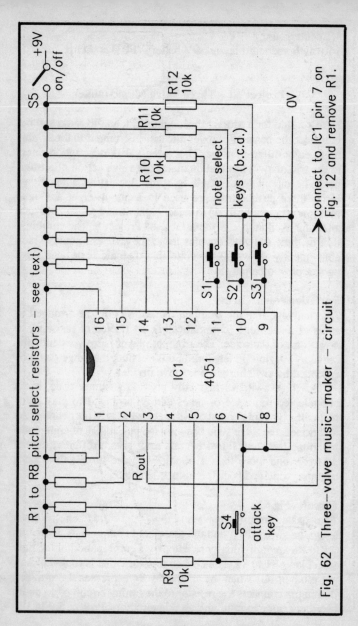

Fig. 62 Three-valve music-maker — circuit

114

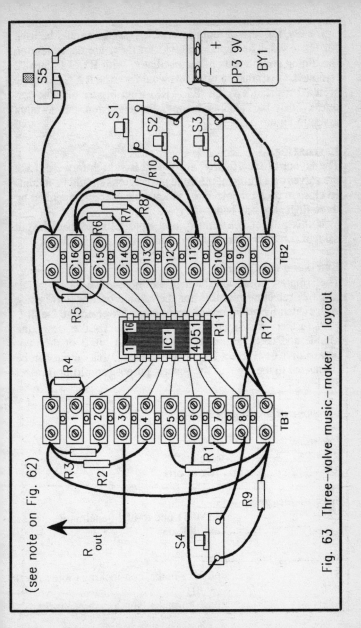

Fig. 63 Three—valve music—maker — layout

(see note on Fig. 62)

115

Ideally, for ease of tuning, variable resistors should be used for R1 to R8. The values required for these are dependent on the timing components of the oscillator. With R1 of Figure 12 removed, the timing components would now be R2, C1, and the selected resistance value (R1 – R8) from Figure 62. The frequency can be calculated approximately from the formula given in Figure 12.

Layout (Fig.63)
The layout of the 16-way breadboard is straightforward. Like the valves on a trumpet, the three pushbuttons should be mounted close to each other in line as they are preferably operated by three fingers of one hand.

If this project is extended, a composite breadboard layout using a common power supply would simplify the wiring.

Extending the Circuit
The simplest practical circuit is the three-valve music-maker (Fig.62) selecting resistors for the astable oscillator (Fig.12), with switch S2 on Figure 12 providing a lower octave facility.

A further experiment is to remove the speaker from the astable and take the output of C3 to input pin 3 of the two-octave divider (Project 29, Fig.60). In turn, this output can be connected to the input of the general-purpose amplifier (Project 26, Fig.54).

Components for Project 30

Resistors
R1 – R8	(see text)
R9 – R12	10k (4 off)

Semiconductor
IC1	CD4051 one-to-eight analogue multiplexer

Switches
S1 – S3	push-to-make, non-locking (note select) (3 off)
S4	push-to-make, non-locking (attack)

Miscellaneous
16-way breadboard layout, 9V battery (PP3) and clip.